COOKING fo

Recipes & I

by

Jo Hampton

It is possible that you, like me, browse through cookbooks looking at the wonderful pictures of foods, cooked and presented by professionals, and feel totally inadequate. Bearing this in mind, I have deliberately prepared and photographed the recipes in this book myself, using only the equipment we have in our very modest kitchen at home. I just followed my own instructions to make sure they made sense. Sometimes it was necessary to improvise because I didn't have the right piece of equipment.

All the recipes worked well and tasted good. The photography may be a little unprofessional to the trained eye, but hopefully has the effect of making the diet look attainable to the average cook.

If I could make all these with no special cookery training or skills then you can too.

ISBN 0 9521544 1 2

© Jo Hampton 1996

All information contained herein was correct at time of going to press.

The Diet Plans and Recipes in this book do not alone constitute a complete anti-Candida programme, but are intended to be used as an integral part of the total regime recommended by Jo Hampton to the sufferers attending her clinic. Whilst the diet is of paramount importance, it is also necessary to give attention to rebuilding the immune system by means of vitamins, minerals and probiotic supplementation, together with antifungal preparations. More extensive details of the full anti-Candida regime can be found in the companion book by the same author entitled; "The Way Back, the A-Z of Coping with M.E., Candida and allergies". ISBN 0 9521544 0 4

If difficulty is experienced in obtaining copies, please contact the publisher.

Kingston House Publishing
Telephone / Fax 01823 35 11 08

Illustrations by:
John Bryant

Typeset in Century Old Style
2nd Edition 2001
Printed by
The Book Factory, 35/37 Queensland Road, London N7 7AH
Tel: 020 7700 1000   Fax: 020 7700 3569

CONTENTS

	Page No.
Introduction	7
What to expect when changing your diet	10
Foods to be excluded from the diet	12
What are Carbohydrates?	15
The Candida Kitchen	16
Where to find your food	18
About the Diet Plan	20

THE DIET

Lists of things you CAN eat.

Meats	23
Fowl	23
Eggs	23
Fish and Seafoods (crustaceans and molluscs)	24
Legumes and pulses	25
Root vegetables	25
Other vegetables including brassicas and gourds	26
Grains	26
Fruits	27

STAGE 1

	Page No.
Introduction to Stage 1	28
Meat eaters diet plan	30
Vegetarian diet plan	31
Blank plan for own use	32

Recipes without fruit and low in carbohydrates

Breakfasts	33
Starters / Lunches	40
Soups and stews	47
Salads	51
Main meals	54
Vegetarian main meals	65
Sauces	71
Desserts	72
Snacks	73
Dips	74
Drinks	77

STAGE 2

	Page No.
Introduction to Stage 2	79
Meat eaters diet plan	80
Vegetarian diet plan	81
Blank plan for own use	82

Recipes with more carbohydrates and fruit included

Breakfasts	83
Starters / Lunches	86
Soups	88
Salads	95
Main meals	102
Vegetarian main meals	111
Desserts	118
Snacks	125
Muffins	128
Waffles	129
Dips	130
Gravy without yeast	131
Breads without yeast	132
Garlic Bread	135
Garlic 'butter'	135
Cakes	138
Biscuits	140
Pastry and dumplings	142-143
Dressings	144
Nuts	146
Drinks	147

STAGE 3   Page No.

Instructions and Eating Plans   148

Eating out   155

Maintaining the diet on holiday   156

Entertaining at home   158

Ideas for practical packed lunches   159

Suggestions for sandwich and pitta fillings   163

Food supplements necessary to complete the programme   164

Where to obtain your supplements   165

Comprehensive list of symptoms   166

Useful addresses   170

Alphabetical index of recipes   173

COOKING FOR CANDIDA

Introduction

Research is progressively showing that Candida albicans is fast becoming a major factor in the decline of good health world-wide.

Every doctor will recognise it as 'thrush', the vaginal problem plaguing so many women. They will also accept it as the white substance found in the mouths of newborn infants, but as yet, few will acknowledge that it can become systemic, moving from the confines of the alimentary tract into the blood stream producing a formidable range of serious physical, mental and emotional problems in men, women and children.

Clinical records show that patients complain of an alarming complexity of symptoms, often affecting every aspect of their health. They suffer memory lapses, poor concentration, fatigue, depression, irritability and headaches. They experience a variety of disturbances of the alimentary tract; poor digestion, constipation and diarrhoea, their vision may fluctuate, they may experience muscle or joint pain or they may have skin conditions such as psoriasis or hives. Often they are distressed by problems involving the reproductive organs; women may show symptoms such as premenstrual tension, menstrual irregularities, persistent vaginitis, endometriosis and infertility; men may suffer impotence and prostatis and both sexes may lose their libido. (sex drive)

These are only a few of the myriad symptoms proving responsive to Candida treatment. It is a very devious condition and is not only causative of the symptoms I have listed above, but is increasingly being shown to have connections with much more serious conditions such as M.E., allergies, multiple sclerosis, Crohn's disease, lupus, bulimia, anorexia nervosa, inflammatory bowel disease, diabetes, epilepsy, cancer and A.I.D.S. There are many more. (See Comprehensive list on page 166)

If, as you read through these symptoms you recognise that one or more of them apply to you, then it is more than possible you have joined the ranks of Candida sufferers seeking relief and advice.

It is important to understand both the nature of Candida itself and its causes if treatment is to be effective. Candida albicans is, as its Latin name implies, a 'white fungus' or yeast. It is a natural inhabitant of the human bowel and, under ordinary circumstances, is confined there by 'friendly flora'. Whilst this proper chemical balance is maintained, the Candida causes no problems. However, if the balance is disturbed and the helpful bacteria are destroyed, then the yeast begins to multiply and travel out of its proper environment, entering the bloodstream and thereby becoming systemic, causing the many and varied health problems described.

The most common cause for the destruction of helpful bacteria is the increasing use of antibiotics, steroids and hormone treatments used both by man himself, and found as residue in the animal flesh he eats. Another major factor is the extensive inclusion of refined carbohydrates and sugars in the modern diet. Other contributors are the use of chemical additives, preservatives and colourants. All this is exacerbated by the levels of stress caused by our modern way of life. In fact, today's lifestyle creates a perfect environment in which the Candida yeast can feed and multiply.

Experience has shown the Candida overgrowth can be corrected naturally and holistically without recourse to drugs of any kind. The sufferer simply needs to adjust their eating habits to starve the overgrowth whilst using antifungal preparations to control any further growth. At the same time the use of vitamin and mineral supplementation will repair the damage sustained to the immune system during the time the Candida overgrowth has been rampant, and probiotics, specially cultured helpful bacteria, will re-establish 'friendly-flora' thus restoring the proper chemical balance. Of course there are many other holistic remedies and therapies that are useful in dealing with localised conditions and help to maintain a positive attitude during the course of the treatment.

Without doubt, the hardest part of the whole procedure is the re-education of your dietary habits. The idea of living on a simple diet, free from sugar, yeast, most dairy products and artificial preservatives seems like the end of the world. Well it isn't. I have drawn together a worldwide selection of foods compatible with

8

the Candida sufferers' needs and will show you exciting ways of preparing them, so opening up a whole new dimension to Candida eating.

This book has been carefully and caringly compiled for everyone with a Candida problem and for those who cater for them, in the certain knowledge that you can, by following the advice given, regain an optimum quality of life. So enjoy.... not only the recipes, but also the vibrant good health that will be yours as a result of using them.

"I have come to know that there is nothing better for them than to rejoice and do good during one's life; and also that every man should eat and indeed drink and see good for all his hard work. It is the gift of God."
(Ecclesiastes 3 v 12 & 13)

WHAT TO EXPECT WHEN YOU CHANGE YOUR DIET

When you decide to eliminate offending foods from your diet, you should be aware that your system may protest. Your eating habits were probably formulated during childhood and by now, all your bodily functions have grown accustomed to a set pattern.

Often it has been noticed how people have unwittingly become dependent on certain foods, or chemicals contained in them, without their knowledge. We have all heard of the 'chocoholic'. It is not just chocolate that can have the effect of 'hooking' a person, many other foods can do the same. It is very often the foods you crave most that have become your personal allergens. Some people suddenly develop allergies to foods they have been eating on a daily basis all their lives. When they cease to consume these substances, they experience withdrawal symptoms or reactions of various kinds. This could happen to you.

The reactions can take physical, mental or emotional form. Physically you could experience severe headaches, stomach cramps and craving for sweet foods. As the Candida is starved of the foods on which it thrives, you may suffer all kinds of aches and pains, bowel disturbances and a general feeling of malaise. You might assume you have influenza because the symptoms are so similar. You could feel as though your brain has been 'switched off', finding it difficult to coordinate your thoughts. Some people have emotional upsets, becoming tearful, argumentative or depressed, even violent. Most if not all of the symptoms you have experienced before, may return all at once, making you feel totally wretched. Don't use this as an excuse to give up on the diet. These are good signs that your body is beginning to respond and cleanse itself of the poisons that have been causing many of your symptoms. Usually this happens when the diet is used in conjunction with a properly balanced vitamin, mineral, antifungal and probiotic programme.* The clinical term for this phase is 'the Herxheimer reaction' or the die off. When this cleansing process is complete, if you continue to eat in the new, healthier style, you will become aware that your symptoms are slowly fading and you will have a much higher energy threshold. You will begin to enjoy life again.

(*see "Food Supplement necessary to complete the programme"
page 164)

*For more information on the clinical aspects of Candida, see the book, 'THE WAY BACK, The A - Z of coping with M.E. Candida and allergies.' by the same author. Published by Kingston House Publishing. ISBN 0 9521544 0 4

FOODS TO BE EXCLUDED FROM THE DIET, AND REASONS WHY

As previously mentioned, the three major foods to be avoided are yeasts, sugars and bovine dairy produce (those made from cows milk). However there are many dietary items that contain, or are in some way connected with these three. They must also be excluded if Candida overgrowth is to be successfully eliminated.

Listed under the three main headings they are:-

SUGARS

This means ALL SUGARS including honey, syrups, glucose, dextrose and for the first month, fructose and all fruits and fruit juices.

YEASTS

Excluding yeast is not easy because it includes all moulds and fungi, also anything based on fermentation. Yeast is found in bread, buns, cakes, biscuits, yeast spreads, (i.e. Marmite, Vecon) gravy powders and stock cubes, soya sauce, miso and tofu. It is also found in alcohol, particularly wines, cider and vinegar, regular shop-bought mayonnaise, Worcestershire sauce, dressings and pickles. Natural yeasts form on grapes, olives, dried fruit, frozen and canned fruits and fruit juices. Only freshly squeezed fruit juice is totally free. Melons, (especially the cantelope variety) oranges, satsumas, tangerines and grapefruit carry moulds in profusion, so peel and scrub them carefully and always wipe the knife clean before cutting them through or you could carry moulds through to contaminate the flesh. Moulds also accumulate readily on hard cheeses if they are matured in muslin, but most significantly abound on blue cheeses such as Danish blue, Stilton, Roquefort and Gorgonzola etc. Tea, coffee and coffee substitutes are also known to collect moulds during the drying process, as does tobacco. Tobacco is a double hazard since, not only does it carry moulds, but it is also cured on sugar. No smoked fish or bacon can be used as it encourages Candida growth.

Fungus forming foods include mushrooms, (which are them selves a fungus), peanuts, pistachios and most other nuts if they are unfresh.

If there are any leftovers after a meal, they should be carefully wrapped and frozen immediately, as moulds will begin to form on them within 24 hours. Refrigerators should be regularly cleaned to curb the formation of moulds.

It is also important to be aware that antibiotics such a mycin, tetracycline, chloromycetin, linococin and penicillin are derived from cultured moulds. Steroid and hormone treatments encourage their growth, therefore, if medication is needed, it is advisable to seek an alternative treatment if you already have a Candida problem. If orthodox treatments cannot be avoided, then seek the advice of a competent alternative practitioner about taking a regular probiotic supplement. B Complex vitamins must be carefully selected as they are often yeast based. They may include thiamine, niacin and riboflavin, however they can now be obtained with a brown rice base that ensures they are yeast free.

Malt is also a common ingredient in prepared products because of its ability to ferment. Not only is it found in beer, whisky and vinegar as you would expect, but it is also an ingredient in breakfast cereals and other packaged foods.

COWS MILK
The main reason why cows milk must be excluded from the diet is because of modern dairy farming techniques. Cows are no longer allowed to graze freely and select their own diet from green fields, but they are fed on specially prepared foods to increase hormonal activity and increase milk yield. They are also frequently subjected to doses of antibiotics and these practices result in contamination of the milk produced for human consumption. Of course this does not affect everyone, only those who are susceptible to yeast overgrowth. Another major reason for avoiding cows milk is because of the high lactose content. Lactose is another form of sugar. As well as the blue cheeses already mentioned, these other foods are derived from cows milk and should be excluded from the diet:-butter, cheeses, cottage cheese, ordinary milk, low fat milk, skimmed milk, butter milk, whey, whey powder, all powdered milks, cream and ice cream.

TAP WATER

Great claims are made for the purity of water, but it can be hazardous in many countries because of the addition of bacteria destroying chemicals, such as chlorine. Remember that the Candida sufferer is trying to increase the population of 'friendly flora' in their system, not cause it to become further depleted, therefore chlorine in drinking water is highly unacceptable. Contamination from nitrates has a very negative effect too, so it is important you use the purest water available to you for both drinking and cooking. A plumbed in filter system will be most beneficial, if not you must buy bottled spring water or a filter jug.

OTHER ITEMS TO AVOID

Because a Candida sufferer's body already has a high toxicity level which is detrimental to healthy immune responses, vigilance should be exercised in selecting foods that are free from artificial additives, colourants and preservatives. Care should also be taken to avoid monosodium glutamate, artificial flavourings and all sweeteners. Tea and coffee should also be avoided because of the caffeine content.

It is also highly destructive to the Candida programme to continue taking birth control pills, antibiotics, steroids, hormones or any immuno - suppressant drugs. While only some of these are actually based on, or derived from yeast, all encourage yeast overgrowth.

Previously mentioned and not to be overlooked is that many Candida sufferers may have developed allergies or intolerances to a variety of foods, peculiar to them alone. It is important to have these sensitivities identified by a competent practitioner so that they also can be excluded from the diet, finding suitable alternative products as substitutes. The recipes in this book are selected with this problem in mind, offering a selection of alternatives wherever possible. A real effort should be made to give up smoking because of its well known damaging effects on health and contribution to Candida overgrowth. For the first month of the programme it is also important to restrict carbohydrate intake.

WHAT ARE CARBOHYDRATES?

Carbohydrates are, according to a dictionary definition, 'kinds of compound of carbon, hydrogen and oxygen essential to living organisms'. In other words, they are necessary to our good health, so why does this book restrict the intake of them for the first month of the diet? There are two kinds of carbohydrate 'complex' which are found in a variety of fruit, vegetables and whole grains, and 'refined' which are present in white flours, sugar, etc.. Whilst both kinds supply energy, only the complex carbohydrates provide the vitamins and minerals that assure proper assimilation by the body. All carbohydrates are changed by body chemistry into sugars and therefore must be restricted if the Candida is to be brought under control, but it is not recommended that they should be cut out entirely for a long period of time, as they are essential to a balanced diet. What should be noted is that the refined carbohydrates are extremely detrimental to health, and because of their extensive use, are one of the contributory causes of the Candida epidemic. So when the diet plan allows the expansion of carbohydrates in the second stage of the diet, make sure to choose the 'complex', unrefined foods beneficial to you, as often as possible.

A list of foods high in carbohydrates
Rice, corn, potatoes, wheat, barley, oats, all grain flours.
Therefore bread, cakes, pastries, pasta, biscuits, pizza, etc., should be restricted until the Candida is coming under control.

THE CANDIDA KITCHEN

In most homes the kitchen is the hub of the household, therefore it should be planned not only for efficiency, but for your comfort. If possible, make room for a chair or stool so that you can sit rather than stand whilst waiting for cooking times. If you are to be successful with the diet you need easy accessibility to the foods and implements you use. Planning is imperative.

Although they are not absolute necessities, a blender and a juicer will make cooking easier for you. An important consideration is to make space in the refrigerator and the freezer, informing the other members of the family who have access to these appliances, that a certain shelf or section is set aside for your exclusive use. You might even choose to label it boldly to avoid confusion. Much time and effort will be spent on selecting suitable foods, it is a course of wisdom to allocate a special cupboard in which to store them. It should be out of the reach of small children and away from the main body of the kitchen. Here too, clear labelling will be helpful. Jewish cooks the world over are familiar with the practice of separating foods (meat and milk) so it is not a new concept, and will become second nature to all quite quickly.

Never put leftover foods away without covering or wrapping them carefully, freezing them immediately whenever possible, making a practice of examining the contents of the refrigerator daily and planning your meals to use the leftovers as soon as practicable. Also be scrupulous about cleanliness; moulds accumulate faster in a kitchen than anywhere else in the house. Particularly vulnerable to mould growth are the areas around the sink, the refrigerator, wooden spoons and chopping boards.

One kitchen requirement that is very important and must not be overlooked is the need to have pure water 'on tap'. Many people manage with a small filter jug with a refill cartridge standing on the draining board. This is adequate if it is all you can afford, but if your budget will allow, it is far more convenient to have a water filter plumbed in under the sink so that the water coming into your kitchen is automatically filtered. There are a number of good models to choose from. For advice as to which one will be suitable

16

for your needs you might choose to contact Penny Davenport or Wholistic Research Co. both of whom are listed in the Useful Addresses on pages 171 and 172.

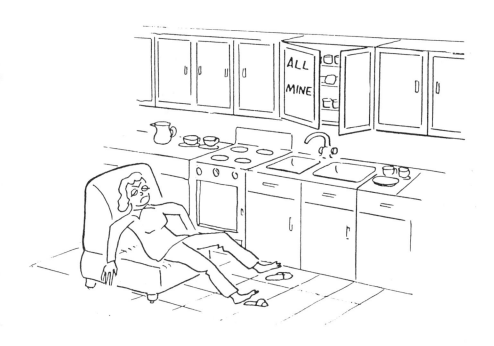

WHERE TO FIND YOUR FOOD

When shopping for a Candida diet, first priority should be given to freshness and the avoidance of chemicals and additives. As far as possible you will be looking for organically produced items. Increasingly Supermarkets around the world are stocking a full range of organic produce with choices of milks and cheeses. Health stores also provide a wonderful range of alternatives. Jewish communities have special shops where 'kosher' foods are available, these can yield a number of interesting items. As the allergy phenomena grows, more and more stores are stocking alternatives as a matter of course. You should experience very few problems finding the things you need if you live within easy reach of a town.

In the countryside you may be even better served. Small villages and outlying districts often have local residents who take pride in being organically self sufficient and are only too happy to sell you some of their produce. The Soil Association has compiled a list of these and will be happy to send you a booklet to help you locate one in your area. (See Useful Addresses Page 170). You may even have enough garden to grow a few vegetables or keep a few chickens for free range eggs yourself. Even in towns it is surprising how much can be grown with very little effort in window boxes or pots and tubs on a small patio. At the very least, fresh herbs can be raised on a kitchen window sill. The satisfaction gained from doing this is health promoting in itself.

Don't forget that hedgerows and woodland can yield a good assortment of fresh foods. Fresh hazel nuts, chestnuts and beech nuts, edible plants such as dandelion leaves for salads, nettles for tea and green vegetable, comfrey for tea and its wonderful healing properties, and fruits and berries such as blackberries and crab-apples in season can be yours for the picking, but make sure you know what you are collecting as some species can be poisonous.

In some rural areas a few of your special dietary needs may have to be ordered specially and sent by post, but there are a number of companies quite prepared to do this. (See Useful Addresses list.) Page 170

Wherever you obtain your food, one thing is of paramount importance. **You must be sure of what it contains,** so ask questions and **read labels** to satisfy yourself that your food not only complies with your dietary requirements as set out in the following diet plan, but is the purest to be found in your area.

ABOUT THE DIET PLAN

Keeping to the diet has always been the most difficult part of following the Candida Control Programme. Sufferers claim they have nothing left to eat, or that the regime is bland and boring. Some say they have difficulty finding things to eat because their thinking is impaired by their illness. This diet plan is designed to take care of all those protests. Most of the thinking has been done for you and if you follow the plan set out, it will be easy. You will eat well planned, interesting meals, with a good nutritional balance and plenty of color and variety. Each recipe has been carefully adapted to exclude the offending ingredients, whilst an effort has been made to offer alternatives to accommodate those having food allergies or sensitivities.

Each sufferer must however, still check to ensure the ingredients do not include one of their individual allergens before making up the chosen recipe. Great care and attention has been exercised to ensure that the essential nutrients are supplied by the diet, as many doctors and practitioners have found that malnutrition has often resulted from an overly restrictive, repetitive diet, therefore only the absolute essentials are left out, and then, only for as long as necessary.

Garlic and olive oil have been included wherever possible. Garlic for its natural antibiotic and cleansing properties and olive oil for the oleic acid which is able to prevent the Candida from altering to its dangerous, myceliel form.* If either of these ingredients is repugnant to you and you prefer to leave them out of the recipes, you are strongly advised to substitute by taking more in a supplementary form along with your vitamins and probiotics etc....

This diet allows dry herbs and spices providing they are selected with care and packaged by a reputable company taking care to guard against moulds, although it is better to use only fresh if possible.

Lemons and limes, both the fruits and their juices are allowed in the first month because they both have very low fructose content. (comparable to that of carrots). They should however be used

* See "The Way Back" Pages 29 - 33

sparingly. Tomatoes, although not strictly classified as fruit are excluded for their high fructose level in the first month but are allowed freely in the second stage.

There is a special section for vegetarian main meals, but many of the other recipes are suitable too, if adapted as suggested.

The diet is set out in three, easy to follow stages and at the start of each section you will find a chart giving you a week of suggested menus. You do not have to follow it exactly to the letter. It is meant as a guide to supply you with ideas. You can change the menu and adapt it to your own personal needs and life style, adding foods you particularly enjoy and dropping things you don't like. What is important is that you keep to the general rules, selecting only the foods allowable in that section, and also remember not to be too repetitive by keeping a good variety going.

STAGE 1

For 1 month
This is the initial stage and it is vital that you keep free from all the foods mentioned under the heading 'Foods to be excluded from the Diet, and Reasons Why.' It also leaves out all fruit and toma-toes and has a low carbohydrate content.

You will probably lose weight during this stage, but don't worry, your weight was probably the result of accumulated toxic waste and you will feel much better without it. As soon as you begin Stage 2 your weight will stabilize. ∧ ∧ *tomotoes are o.k. according to kitty.*

STAGE 2

For 5 months (approximately)
Allows fruit and tomatoes back into the diet and expands the carbohydrate intake, although it is sensible to keep it fairly low. Particularly if you prefer to continue loosing weight. Also for those who are sure, after testing, that they can tolerate them, goats and sheeps cheeses can be added. This stage lasts for 5 months, or until all initial symptoms have gone and tests* confirm that Candida is under control.

STAGE 3

For the rest of your life

This section includes a series of charts to help you reintroduce foods that have been either excluded or restricted from the diet, in such a way as to avoid a return to poor eating habits and a reoccurrence of the Candida over growth.

Before starting the diet

Before embarking on the diet, it would be beneficial to have allergy tests carried out by a competent practitioner,* then, armed with the list of foods you personally must avoid, go through the book and select the recipes most suited to your needs. Mark them and/or adjust the ingredients to fit your individual requirements. For example, where goats, sheeps or soya milk are listed, cross through the ones you cannot tolerate, or if tests reveal you to be allergic to onions, go through and replace onions with leeks, or garlic in the recipes. In this way you can adapt the book to suit your own personal needs and use.

Do remember that **ALL the water used** to make up the recipes must be **filtered or bottled spring water.**

All margarines must be dairy free.

All cheeses MUST be made only with sheeps or goats milk and matured in wax rather than muslin. (muslin encourages moulds)

All eggs should be free range.

Meats should be free range, organically reared wherever possible.

If cling film is to be used, do make sure that it is non PVC meaning it will be non carcinogenic. (non cancer forming)

As has already been stated, the emphasis throughout the diet is on fresh, whole foods, uncontaminated by additives, chemicals and preservatives, organically grown if possible.

Now for what you can eat!

Bon appétit!

* The tests referred to here are by means of Applied Kinesiology or a Vega machine.

A COMPREHENSIVE LIST OF FOODS YOU CAN EAT IN STAGE 1

Meat

Some people will eat anything

alligator	goat	rabbit and hare
beef (gelatin)	kangaroo	squirrel
bison	lamb	veal
buffalo	mutton	venison
elk	ostrich	wild boar
frog (legs)	pork (ham & bacon unsmoked)	

All internal organs of these animals are also edible i.e., heart, liver, kidneys etc. Tripe and trotters and other parts of the animal are also acceptable. Any by-products such as burgers, sausages and prepared meats should be vetted carefully to ensure contents do not include additives, preservatives and yeast (rusk).

Fowl

bantam	grouse	pheasant
birds (small, wild)	guinea fowl	pigeon
chicken	partridge	quail
duck	peacock	turkey
goose		

All meat and fowl should, if at all possible, be free range organically reared.

Eggs

bantam	goose	quail
chicken	guinea fowl	turtle
duck		

All eggs should be free range.

Fish

abalone	hake	shark
anchovy	halibut	shrimp
bass	harvest fish	skate
bluefish	herring	smelt
bream	ling	snails
brill	lobster	sole
butterfish	mackerel	squid
carp	monkfish	sturgeon
catfish	mullet	sunfish
caviar	mussels	swordfish
clams	oyster	trout
cockles	perch	tuna
cod	plaice	tunny
crab	pompano	turbot
crappie	prawn	whale
crayfish	red snapper	whelks
croaker	rock salmon	whitebait
dace	rose fish	whitefish
eel	sail fish	whiting
fish roe	sardine	winkles
flounder	scallop	
haddock	scampi	

Legumes and Pulses

Beans	Peas	Lentils
azuki	blackeye (cowpea)	pink
black	chick pea (garbanzo)	plain green
butter	purple hull	
fava	snap	
french dwarf	split	
kidney		
lima	**Seeds**	
navy	alfalfa	
soy	caraway	
string	pine kernels	
masur	poppy	
mung (bean & sprouts)	pumpkin	
snap	sesame	
stick	sunflower	
tonka bean		

Root Vegetables

anise	kohlrabi	rutabaga
artichokes (Jerusalem, Sunchokes)	onion	spring onion
beetroot	parsnip	swede
carrot	parsley root	sweet potato*
celeriac	potato (Irish)*	turnip
celery	radish onion	yam

* Restricted during the first month

Other Vegetables including brassicas and gourds

artichoke (globe)
asparagus
bok choy
broccoli (calabrese)
brussel sprouts
cabbage (all varieties)
cauliflower
celery
chickory
chilli
chives
collards
cress
cucumber
dandelion leaves
egg plant (aubergine)

endive
escarole
jícama
kale
leeks
lettuce (all varieties)
marrow (squash)
mustard greens
nettles
okra
parsley
pea (fresh)
pea pods
pea (sugar snap)
peppers (capsicum/bell)
pumpkin

purple sprouting
red cabbage
scallions
spinach
spring greens
sprouts
sprout tops
squash (marrow)
summer savoury
sunflower greens
Swiss chard
tomato*
turnip tops
vine leaves
watercress
zucchini (courgette)

* Restricted during the first month

Grains (These are restricted during the first month)

amaranth
bamboo shoots
barley
buckwheat
corn (maize)
couscous
flaxseed

maize (corn)
millet
oats
oat bran
psyllium (seeds & husks)
rice
rye

sorghum
sprouted wheat,
sprouted barley,
sprouted rye
wheat

Fruits (None for the first month)

apple
apricot
avocado
banana
Barbados cherry
bearberry
bilberry
blackberry
blueberry
boysenberry
breadfruit
cantaloupe
caper
casaba melon
cherry
Chinese gooseberry
crabapple
cranberry
currant
damson
date
dewberry

elderberry
fig
gooseberry
grapefruit
greengage
ground cherry
guava
honeydew melon
huckleberry
Japanese persimmon
kiwi
lemon
lime
loganberry
longberry
lychee
mango
mulberry
muskmelon
nectarine
orange
papaya

passionfruit
pawpaw
peach
pear
persimmon
pineapple
plums
pomegranate
prickley pear
quince
raspberry
redcurrant
rhubarb
rosehip
satsuma
sloe
starfruit
strawberry
tangerine
watermelon
wineberry
youngberry

Never again say, "There's nothing to eat."

Now let me introduce the eating plan that is going to help restore your health.

STAGE 1

STAGE 1 (For 1 month)

It is critically important to get this first stage of the diet exactly right if the initial "die off." or Herxheimer is to take place properly. Although it has already been mentioned in full detail, I am going to repeat a list of foods to be avoided to add extra emphasis to the importance of them. They are, in brief, yeasts, moulds, bovine dairy produce, all sugars, fruit and chemicals. At the same time the carbohydrate content must be kept low.

There is a sample menu plan for 1 week to help you. One for meat eaters and one for vegetarians. You will notice that the main carbo-hydrate allowance is at breakfast time. Some recommend the exclusion of all carbohydrate, but as one of the foremost symp-toms is fatigue, with absolutely no carbohydrate, body energy could fall to a dangerous low. However, it is still important to keep to only one carbohydrate meal each day.

If you find it easiest to follow the plan exactly as it is, then do so, but if you need to change it to comply with personal allergens or eating times, then feel free to adjust it to your individual needs. A blank chart is included for this purpose. You may use any of the recipes included in this section and add some of your own ideas as long as they exclude "forbidden" items.

Two things should be mentioned here. The first is to remind you that this is not a slimming diet, so eat as much as you like of the foods you are allowed, by increasing the size of your portions, you will alleviate the desire to snack between meals. Secondly, if you do become extraordinarily hungry and feel you must snack, make yourself an omelette, **don't choose a chocolate bar.** The latter will do untold damage to the entire plan. Try not to break the rules, after all it is only for 30 days.

One last point, if you go out to work, it is vital to plan and prepare ahead for midday meals.

* For vegetarian carbohydrate planning - see note on page 65
Many of the recipes are suitable, or adaptable for vegetarian use
and are clearly marked.

The news of the connection between B.S.E. and C.J.D. broke just
as this book was about to go to press. We contemplated replacing
all the recipes containing beef, but since it only applies in Britain,
we decided to leave them in and suggest alternatives for those
needing to substitute until beef is available again from uncontaminated sources.

MEAT EATERS DIET PLAN

	BREAKFAST	LUNCH	DINNER
MONDAY	Kashi (commercially available cereal) with Soya, goats or sheeps milk. Herb tea	Chicken Stew (in a flask if going out)	Cold meat salad (with roast leftovers) or Rabbit with Mustard Sauce **NO POTATOES**
TUESDAY	Porridge (oats, millet, sorgum) Herb tea	Falafel and Salad (wrap Falafel & take salad in a plastic tub) to take out. Pilchards or prawns (tinned) Don't forget tin opener	Scandinavian Mackerel or Stuffed Marrow with veg of choice **NO POTATOES**
WEDNESDAY	2 Fried eggs on pitta bread & bacon Herb tea	Hummus and Crudites (carry in plastic containers if going out)	Lambs Liver and Onions with veg or Cauliflower Cheese **NO POTATOES**
THURSDAY	Puffed rice (commercially available) with soya, goats or sheeps milk. Herb tea	Coleslaw and tinned tuna fish (tuna stays in tin, coleslaw in plastic container) don't forget tin opener if going out	Savoury Mince and vegetables **NO POTATOES**
FRIDAY	Home made muesli with soya, goats or sheeps milk Herb tea	Greek Vegetable Soup (in a flask if going out)	Haddock with Cheese and Leek Sauce and vegetables of choice. Parsnip chips **NO POTATOES**
SATURDAY	Scrambled eggs on pitta bread Herb tea	Cretan Feta Cheese Salad (sheeps cheese wrapped seperately if going out) salad in a plastic container	Steak with large mixed salad or Trout with Almonds & Salad **NO POTATOES**
SUNDAY	Hearty start or fish cakes Herb tea	Avocado with Prawns (all ingredients can be packed seperately and put together at time of eating if going out)	Roast with Vegetables **NO POTATOES**

30

VEGETARIAN DIET PLAN

	BREAKFAST	LUNCH	DINNER
MONDAY	(Carbohydrate adjustment) Live goats or sheeps yogurt	Falafel and Salad (wrap Falafel & take salad in a plastic tub) to take out	Aduki Bean Crumble **NO POTATOES**
TUESDAY	Porridge (oats, millet, sorgum) Herb tea	Chilled Cucumber and Yogurt Soup (in flask if going out)	Stuffed Marrow with vegetarian stuffing **NO POTATOES**
WEDNESDAY	Swiss Rösti Potatoes Herb tea	Hummous and Crudites (carry in plastic containers if going out)	Cauliflower Cheese **NO POTATOES**
THURSDAY	Scrambled eggs on pitta bread Herb tea	Coleslaw and goats cheese packed with salad	Mixed Vegetable Stir Fry **NO POTATOES**
FRIDAY	(Carbohydrate adjustment) Live goats or sheeps yogurt	Watercress Soup (in a flask if going out)	Spinach and Soft Sheeps Cheese Quiche vegetables of choice **NO POTATOES**
SATURDAY	Home-made muesli with soya, goats or sheeps milk Herb tea	Cretan Feta Cheese Salad (sheeps cheese wrapped seperately if going out) salad in a plastic container	Mixed Bean Salad **NO POTATOES**
SUNDAY	Onion Hash Browners Herb tea	Egg Mayonnaise (in plastic container if going out)	Spinach Timbale **NO POTATOES**

BLANK FOR OWN USE

	BREAKFAST	LUNCH	DINNER
MONDAY			
TUESDAY			
WEDNESDAY			
THURSDAY			
FRIDAY			
SATURDAY			
SUNDAY			

BREAKFASTS

Breakfast seems to be the meal that Candida sufferers have most difficulty with. Some say it is because they don't have enough options, and others complain they are totally incapable of organising themselves first thing in the morning because of the fuzzy headed feeling they experience. Here are a few suggestions to make it easier.

If you are satisfied with just a bowl of cereal, then there are several quite adequate, commercially prepared breakfast cereals available, but do watch packaging continually for changes in ingredients.

Light Breakfast

Shredded Wheat* See Footnote

Puffed Wheat

Kashti (a mixture of whole grains and sesame)   Health shops only

Puffed rice   Health shops only

At the time of writing all of these products were available, sugar free.

They can all be eaten either dry or with goats, sheeps or soya milk.

The Big Breakfast

For others who need a more substantial breakfast, these cereals may only be a 'starter'. If you have to go out to work, or for some other reason have problems finding the right things to eat in the middle of the day, it is wise to have a really big breakfast. This will not only ensure that you are not tempted to snack on the wrong foods, but will also give you energy to burn throughout the day and may even suffice until you can get home to enjoy a proper evening meal.

The following recipes will help you.

---

* The author and publishers can take no responsibility for the withdrawal of commercially prepared items mentioned

Asparagus Omelette

4 asparagus spears

2 tablespoons chopped onion

2 tablespoons olive oil

4 free range eggs

½ teaspoon minced garlic

sea salt and pepper

Method

Steam the asparagus for 2 minutes until tender crisp. Reserve 2 of the asparagus spears and slice the other 2 into pieces diagonally. Beat the eggs and add the asparagus, salt and pepper to taste. Heat the oil in an omelette pan, add the onion and garlic. Cook until onion is soft but not brown. Stir in the egg mixture and cook until almost solid. Place the 2 remaining asparagus spears across the centre of the omelette and fold in half. Cover and cook for approx 1½ minutes over a low heat. Serve immediately

Suitable for vegetarians   Serves 1

Onion Hash Browners

4 large, precooked, peeled potatoes

1 large onion, chopped finely

1 teaspoon finely chopped, fresh sage (optional)

4 tablespoons (60ml) dairy free margarine

sea salt and pepper

Method

Melt the margarine in a frying pan and lightly cook the onions until they are soft. When they are done, remove from the pan with a slotted spoon taking care to remove as little of the margarine as possible. Spread on kitchen paper to cool. Grate the potatoes through the largest section of grater into a bowl. Add the cooked onions, sage and salt and pepper to taste. Mix well together. Form into shapes and return to the frying pan. Cook over medium high heat for 10 to 12 minutes until golden brown, turn over and repeat on the other side. Remove from pan and place on serving dish with a sprig of sage to garnish. Serve hot.

Suitable for vegetarians   Serves 4

Swiss Style Muesli

225g (8oz) rolled oats   225g (8oz) barley flakes

½ cup pumpkin seeds   ½ cup blanched, flaked almonds

sesame seeds, sunflower seeds, pine kernels, bran, wheatgerm - mixed according to taste

Method

Place all the ingredients in a large bowl and mix well. Transfer to an airtight tin or other airtight container to store. Use as required. Serve with goats, sheeps or soya milk.

Fresh fruit may be added after the first month.

Suitable for vegetarians

Brown Rice Porridge

100g (4oz) brown rice flakes   500ml (1pt) water

Method

Stir the rice and water together in a saucepan and bring to the boil. Reduce heat and simmer, stirring occasionally, for 5 - 10 minutes. Serve immediately with a small amount of goats, sheeps or soya milk to add creamy texture.

Suitable for vegetarians   Serves 2

Polenta (Maizemeal Porridge)

100g (4oz) maizemeal   500ml (1pt) water

pinch of sea salt

Method

Blend maizemeal and a little of the water to a smooth paste. Boil the rest of the water in a heavy based pan. Stir in the maizemeal mixture. Bring back to the boil, stirring continuously until it is smooth. Cover and simmer gently for 15 minutes. Serve with goats, sheeps or soya milk.

(After 1st month sliced fresh fruit may be added).

Suitable for vegetarians   Serves 2

Swiss Rösti Potatoes <small>pictured page 97</small>

4 large potatoes, scrubbed, baked in skins

4 tablespoons (60ml) dairy free margarine

salt and pepper

sprig of fresh rosemary

Method

Potatoes should be cold, preferably cooked the night before, wrapped and stored in the refrigerator. When potatoes are cold, carefully peel off the skins. Grate them by hand using the largest section of metal grater, or use largest disc on food grater. Heat the margarine in a 25cm (10inch) frying pan over a medium heat until melted. Press the grated potatoes evenly into the frying pan. (Do not stir or turn the potatoes). Season with salt and pepper to taste. Cook for 10 to 12 minutes until golden brown. Turn the potatoes onto a plate. Garnish and serve.

Suitable for vegetarians   Serves 4

Farmhouse Scramble <small>pictured page 37</small>

3 free range eggs   sea salt

ground white pepper

100g (4oz) lean chopped bacon (unsmoked)

2 tablespoons goats, sheeps or soya milk

Method

Place the bacon in a small frying pan and fry gently until the fat runs, stirring continuously. Fry for a further 4 minutes, then remove from the pan with a slotted spoon and keep hot.Crack the eggs into a bowl. Add the milk, salt and pepper to taste and whisk lightly with a fork until mixed. Pour into the pan and cook gently until the eggs are set to your liking. Stir the bacon into the egg mixture and turn out over 2 Welsh cakes, sliced yeast free bread or pitta bread. (see breads section p 132). Serve immediately.

* **Adjustable for vegetarians**   Serves 2

Vegetarians leave out bacon

Farmhouse Scramble Recipe page 36

Herb Fish Cakes Recipe page 39

Herb Fish Cakes <small>pictured page 38</small>

900g (2lb) potatoes, scrubbed and peeled

700g (1½lb) white fish (cod, haddock, whiting etc)

50g (2oz) dairy free margarine

1 teaspoon oregano, fine chopped or dried

1 teaspoon parsley, fine chopped or dried

½ teaspoon sea salt

a shake of pepper

oil of choice for frying

sprig of parsley to garnish

a little potato flour (different flours may be used if desired)

Method

Place the potatoes in a pan and cover with water. Bring to the boil and cook for about 15 to 20 minutes, or until they are done. Drain and place in a large mixing bowl. While the potatoes are cooking, place the fish in a skillet or poaching pan and cover with water. Bring to the boil and then simmer gently for approximately 5 minutes until the fish turns opaque and will separate from the skin easily. Drain and remove skin and any bones that may be left in the flesh, flaking the fish into small pieces. Set aside. Mash the potatoes adding the margarine. Combine the mashed potatoes, fish, oregano, parsley, salt and pepper and continue mashing until all ingredients are well mixed.

Place a little flour on a plate and divide the fish and potato mixture into 10 portions. Form into round cakes on the floured plate. Heat a little oil in a frying pan and fry the fish cakes on both sides until golden brown. Serve garnished with a sprig of fresh parsley.

Makes 10

Note.

These fish cakes freeze well. For the best results when freezing, do not complete the recipe above but instead of frying at the end, wrap separately and freeze immediately when completely cold. Fry when defrosted, before serving.

STARTERS AND LUNCHES

Avocado with Dressed Prawns

2 ripe avocados, sliced in halves and stones removed

100g (4oz) frozen peeled prawns, thawed

4 tablespoons Greek Island Dressing (page 144)

4 slices lemon and 1 teaspoon chopped parsley to garnish

Method

Place the halved pears into individual serving dishes and divide the prawns into the hollow left by the stone. Spoon 1 tablespoon of dressing over each one and sprinkle with the parsley. Cut the lemon slices half way across and hang them over the side of each individual dish. Serve.

Serves 4 as a starter but only 1 for lunch

Egg Mayonnaise

4 hard boiled eggs, shelled (free range)

4 lettuce leaves	sea salt
black pepper	1 tablespoon chopped chives

For the mayonnaise

2 egg yolks	½ teaspoon dried mustard
300ml (½pt) olive oil	1 tablespoon lemon juice

Method

Slice the eggs in half lengthways. Place a lettuce leaf on each serving plate, sprinkle with salt and pepper and lay two egg halves on each, cut side down.

To make mayonnaise, place the egg yolks in a cool mixing bowl with the mustard and salt and pepper to taste. Beat together, add the oil, drop by drop at first, beating continuously. As the mixture begins to thicken, the oil can be added faster until it can be drizzled in a thin steady stream. Finish by beating in the lemon juice. Spoon the mayonnaise over the eggs and sprinkle with the chopped chives. (Serve with yeast free bread, spread with dairy free margarine, after first month).

Suitable for vegetarians   Serves 4 as a starter but only 1 for lunch

Falafel

250g (8oz) chick peas, (garbanzo beans) soaked overnight
4 spring onions, chopped
2 cloves garlic, chopped
3 tablespoons water
3 large parsley sprigs
½ teaspoon ground cumin
sea salt and pepper
olive oil for deep frying

Method
Drain the chick peas and cover with water in a pan. Bring to the boil and cook for 20 minutes. The peas should not be too soft. Drain and place in a blender or food processor with garlic, onions, water and parsley. Work until the mixture becomes a purée. Add the remaining ingredients and blend for a further 10 seconds. Turn out into a bowl and cover with a cloth. Leave to dry out for 1 - 2 hours. Roll the mixture between the hands to form walnut sized balls, then flatten slightly. Heat the oil in a deep fryer and add the falafel, in batches, frying each batch for about 4 minutes, until golden. Drain on kitchen paper and serve hot with a side salad or mayonnaise (see page 146)

Suitable for vegetarians   Serves 4

Note.
Just Wholefoods make a good Organic Falafel mix. They are willing to supply by post. (See useful addresses page 170).

Oeufs Florentine <small>pictured page 43</small>

¾ kg (1½lb) spinach, washed & trimmed

sea salt	pinch of grated nutmeg
4 eggs	50g (2oz) sheeps cheddar
25g (1oz) dairy free margarine	pepper

Method

Wash the spinach and put in a large saucepan with the salt to taste. Heat gently until the juices flow from the spinach, then cover and cook gently for 5 - 10 minutes until spinach collapses and is tender (no need to add water). Drain and chop. Return to rinsed out pan with the margarine, nutmeg and pepper to taste, and allow to dry out for a few minutes over a gentle heat. Meanwhile, lightly poach the eggs in gently simmering fitered or spring water. Divide spinach into 4 individual flameproof dishes (or 2 flameproof plates if serving as a lunch). Place the drained poached eggs on top and sprinkle with cheese. Melt under a pre-heated grill for 2 - 3 minutes.
Serve immediately.

Suitable for vegetarians   Serves 2 - 4

Greek Hummus <small>pictured page 44</small>

175g (6oz) chick peas (garbanzo beans) soaked overnight

juice of 2 large lemons	2 cloves of garlic, crushed
100ml (1fl. oz) tahini paste	sea salt and pepper
15ml (1 tablespoon) sesame oil	pinch of cayenne pepper

Method

Cook the chick peas until tender. Drain, cool and purée in a blender with lemon juice, garlic, tahini, seasoning and oil. Serve sprinkled with cayenne and crudités.

(You can add pitta bread when you reach Stage 2)

Suitable for vegetarians   Serves 4

Oeufs Florentine Recipe page 42

Greek Hummus Recipe page 42

Pitta Bread Recipe page 132

Fish Roe Stuffed Eggs

8 hard boiled eggs, shelled (free range)

150ml (¼pt) yogurt (goats or sheeps)

100g (4oz) ½ cup lumpfish roe (fresh or tinned)

juice of 1 lemon

sea salt

freshly ground black pepper

Method

Cut the eggs in half lengthwise, then remove the yolks. Place the yolks in a bowl with the yogurt and lemon juice, and mash well together. Work in the fish roe, season to taste.

Pile into the egg whites and serve on a bed of lettuce.

Serves 4 as a starter - 2 for lunch

Cretan Feta Cheese Salad

2 large tomatoes, quartered and sliced in wedges

1 cos lettuce, torn into pieces   75ml (5 tablespoons) olive oil

½ cucumber, sliced   12 thin slices feta cheese

1 red onion, sliced and chopped   sea salt and pepper

1 green bell pepper, seeded and sliced

30ml (2 tablespoons) dried or fresh chopped oregano

Method

Mix the salad vegetables together in a bowl. Toss gently in the oil and season to taste. Top with sprinkled herb and feta cheese slices.

Note.

When you reach stage 2 you may add pitta bread on the side.

In stage 3 add about 10 black olives to restore the recipe to a truly authentic Greek salad.

Suitable for vegetarians   Serves 4

Whitebait

¼kg (8oz) whitebait , washed   freshly ground black pepper

flour for coating   oil of choice for deep frying

sea salt   lemon slices to finish

Method

Coat the fish in the flour seasoned with salt and pepper. Heat the oil in a deep fat fryer until it is really hot (180-190°C / 350-375°F on deep fry thermometer). Using the frying basket, add the fish in small batches, shaking the basket occasionally to ensure they do not stick together while cooking. Fry until golden brown, usually 2 - 3 minutes. Remove the fish from the pan, drain on kitchen paper and keep warm until all the fish are fried, garnish with the lemon slices and serve hot, with thin slices of yeast free sandwich bread and a small green salad. (Yeast free bread should only be used after the first month, until then make the salad larger).

Serves 2

Baba Ghanoush

1 large aubergine   2 cloves garlic, crushed

2 tablespoons tahini   juice of 1 lemon

¼ teaspoon ground cumin   1 tablespoon chopped parsley

sea salt and pepper to taste   sprigs of parsley to garnish

Method

Prick aubergine all over with a fork, cut in half and place cut side down, on grill pan rack. Place under pre-heated low grill until the skin is black and starts to blister and the flesh feels soft. Peel and wash the aubergine and squeeze out as much juice as possible as this is rather bitter. Chop the aubergine flesh and place it in a blender with the garlic and blend to a purée. Add the tahini and the lemon juice alternately, blending between each addition. Turn into a bowl and stir in the cumin, parsley, sea salt and pepper to taste. Turn into a shallow serving dish and garnish with the parsley sprigs. (Serve with yeast free pitta bread, after 1st month. Until then use as a dip with crudités. See page 74).

Suitable for vegetarians   Serves 2 as starter 1 as lunch

SOUPS

Creamy Carrot Soup

250g (8oz) carrots

100g (4oz) leeks (white part only)

275ml (½pt) yeast free vegetable stock

125ml (5 fl. oz) goats or sheeps yogurt

½teaspoon ground mace

sea salt and pepper to taste

Method

Slice the carrots and put into a pan together with the leeks and vegetable stock. Bring to the boil and simmer until tender. Place in a blender and liquidize, add salt and pepper to taste. Stir in the yogurt and return to the heat. Heat through, taking care not to allow it to boil. Serve hot or chilled.

Suitable for vegetarians   Serves 2

Chicken and Leek Soup

1 chicken carcass with any leftover chicken, diced

3 leeks, washed, halved and sliced lengthwise

1 bouquet garni

sea salt and pepper

Method

Place the chicken carcass and leftover meat into a large saucepan, cover with water and add salt and pepper to taste and bouquet garni. Bring to the boil. Lower the heat, cover and simmer for 2 hours, skimming with a slotted spoon when necessary to remove any scum that forms. Add more liquid if the water in the pan becomes too low. 20 minutes before the end of the cooking time add the prepared leeks. Before serving, remove the carcass from the pan and make sure that every scrap of meat is in the soup. Skim again with an ordinary spoon to remove any further scum and fat. Use absorbent kitchen roll to remove any stubborn fat. Remove bouquet garni. Test for seasoning and serve hot.

Serves 4

Chilled Cucumber and Yogurt Soup

400g (14oz) goats or sheeps yogurt

8cm or 3inch length of cucumber, chopped fine or grated

2 spring onions, chopped finely

1 dessertspoon finely chopped fresh mint

1 clove garlic, crushed

2 to 4 tablespoons goats, sheeps or soya milk

sea salt and pepper to taste

Method

Place the yogurt in a large bowl and stir in all the other ingredients. The type of milk will depend on the kind of yogurt you choose and the amount of milk you will need will vary depending on the thickness of the yogurt. Chill for about 1 hour. Serve garnished with a little chopped mint. Some prefer this soup without the garlic.

Suitable for vegetarians serves 2

Celery Soup

2 heads of celery

700ml (1¼pt) water

1 garlic clove, finely chopped

3 tablespoons vegetable oil of choice

275ml (½pt) goats, sheeps or soya milk

1 large leek, white part only, cut into 1cm (½inch) pieces

pinch of pepper

¼ teaspoon sea salt

Method

Cut the leaves from the heads of celery and place them in a saucepan with the water. Bring to the boil, then lower the heat and simmer for 20 minutes. Strain the celery leaf liquid into a jug and set aside, discarding the leaves. Cut the celery stalks into 1cm (½inch) pieces. Wash the saucepan and dry it well. Heat the oil in it and add the celery and leek pieces, frying them continuously for 5 to 7 minutes until they are soft but not brown. Stir in the leaf liquid and garlic and bring to the boil. Reduce heat and simmer for 40 minutes. Add salt and pepper to taste and stir in the milk. Simmer for a further 5 minutes, stirring occasionally. Serve hot.

Suitable for vegetarians Serves 4

Greek Vegetable Soup

450ml (¾pt) beef stock (yeast free) or   vegetable / chicken stock
100g (4oz) mixed vegetables, chopped
300ml (½pt) goats or sheeps yogurt
finely grated rind of well scrubbed lemon
1 egg yolk   freshly ground black pepper
sea salt   1 tablespoon chopped mint

Method

Place the stock in a pan and bring to the boil. Add the vegetables, then lower the heat, cover and simmer for 10 minutes or until tender. Meanwhile, put the egg yolk in a bowl and whisk in the yogurt. Stir in 6 tablespoons of the hot liquid and mix well. Add to the soup in the pan, stirring continuously, then heat through gently without boiling. Season with salt and pepper to taste. Pour into 4 individual bowls and garnish with chopped mint and lemon rind. Serve hot

Serves 4.

Watercress Soup

2 bunches of watercress, trimmed
150ml (¼pt) goats or sheeps yogurt   1 tablespoon olive oil
600ml (1pt) yeast free chicken stock   2 egg yolks
1 small onion, peeled and finely chopped sea salt and white pepper

Method

Remove 16 leaves from the watercress and reserve for the garnish. Chop the remaining watercress and stems. Heat the oil in a pan, add the onion and fry gently until soft and golden. Add the watercress and the stock and bring to the boil. Lower the heat, cover and simmer for 20 minutes. Rub the soup through a sieve (strainer), or work to a purée in an electric blender. Put the egg yolks in a bowl and whisk in the yogurt. Stir in 4 tablespoons of the purée and mix well. Pour the remaining purée into the rinsed pan. Add the yogurt mixture, stirring constantly, then heat through gently without boiling. Season to taste. Pour into individual bowls and garnish with the reserved watercress leaves. This soup is also good chilled.

Suitable for vegetarians

Chicken Stew

leftover chicken carcass

1 large carrot

1 large onion

1 small turnip

1 medium parsnip

sea salt and pepper

1 litre (2⅓pts) water

fresh herbs if available

2 teaspoons yeast free stock powder

Method

Place the chicken carcass in a large pan, cover and bring to the boil, lower the heat and simmer for 1½ hours. Remove from the heat and remove the carcass. Leave the stock to stand until fat has settled on the top and then skim and discard the fat. When the carcass is cool, pick all the small edible pieces of chicken from it and put back into the stock. Dice all the vegetables and add to the stock. Add the stock powder, seasoning and herbs and bring to the boil. Reduce heat and simmer for 10 - 15 minutes, or until vegetables are soft. Serve immediately or transfer to thermos flask to keep hot for use later in the day.

Note.

This is a nourishing way of using up any meat leftovers, instead of making the stock from the chicken carcass, as described above, use vegetable water and brawn from the roasting tin to form the basis for your stew, making sure that all the dripping is removed. If made in quantity this stew can be placed in freezer proof sealed containers and frozen in individual portions for later use. You may also use any number of fresh vegetables to add variety, e.g. brussel sprouts, broad beans, split peas, and after the first month the flavour is enhanced by a tablespoon of tomato purée, or the addition of a segmented orange.

Serves 4 - 6

SALADS

Salads with carbohydrate content are intended for use as main meals and breakfast should be adjusted as recommended on page 65

King Prawn or Scampi and Jícama Salad

340 g (¼lb) (about 8) large raw prawns (prepared)

3 tablespoons oil of choice	2 tablespoons minced garlic
3 spring onions, thinly sliced	3 tablespoons lemon juice

(If jícama is unavailable in your area, use courgettes (zacchini) instead, but after preparing, leave sprinkled with salt for 30 minutes before use.)

Salad Ingredients

1 jícama	a pinch of chilli powder
1 small cucumber, unpared	3 tablespoons vegetable oil
½ teaspoon grated lime peel	6 lettuce leaves, washed
1 clove minced garlic	lemon and lime slices for garnish
¼ teaspoon sea salt	2ml (2 tablespoons) fresh lime juice

1 red skinned onion very finely sliced into slivers

Method

Peel jícama. Cut lengthwise into 8 wedges; cut wedges crosswise into 3mm (⅛inch) slices to form triangles. Cut cucumber in half lengthwise, scoop out the seed and discard. Cut halves crosswise into 3mm (⅛ inch) slices making half moon type shapes. Combine jícama, cucumber and onion in a large bowl; toss lightly. Combine lime juice, lime peel, minced garlic, salt and chilli powder in a small bowl. Gradually add oil, whisking continuously to blend. Pour dressing over salad, toss lightly to coat. Cover and refrigerate 1 to 2 hours to blend the flavours.

Allow (approximately) 15 minutes before serving time to cook the prawns. Place oil in a frying pan over medium heat. Add the garlic; cook and stir for 1 to 2 minutes until softened but not brown. Add the prawns, spring onions and lemon juice; cook, stirring continuously until the prawns turn pink and are firm. About 1 to 2 minutes each side. DO NOT OVERCOOK.

Make up the meal by arranging the lettuce leaves around a large serving dish. Place the salad in the middle and arrange the cooked prawns on the top. Garnish with lemon and lime slices. Serve while still hot.

Hot Chinese Chicken Salad

8 boneless chicken thighs

25g (1oz) cornflour

3 tablespoons olive oil

1 can water chestnuts

8 radishes, sliced

1 clove crushed garlic

lemon slices for garnish

2 sticks celery, diagonally sliced

1 finely shredded Iceberg lettuce

½ teaspoon ground ginger

1 small bunch green (spring) onions, coarsely chopped

Method

Cut the chicken into bite size pieces; set aside. Place the cornflour in a shallow dish. Roll the chicken in the cornflour until each piece is evenly coated. shake off the excess; set aside.

Place a wok or large frying pan over a high heat. Heat the oil, swirling to coat the wok or pan. Add chicken and stir fry until it is no longer pink in the middle, (approximately 3 minutes). Stir in the water chestnuts, onion, celery, radishes, garlic and ground ginger. Stir well. Cover and simmer for 5 minutes. Arrange lettuce on 4 serving plates and heap the chicken mixture on top. Garnish with the lemon. Serve immediately with plain boiled rice.

Serves 4

Mixed Bean Salad

75g (3oz) red kidney beans - soaked overnight

75g (3oz) haricot beans - soaked overnight

3 tablespoons garlic dressing (see page 145)

2 tablespoons chopped parsley   75g (3oz) fresh broad beans

75g (3oz) fresh French beans   sea salt

Method

Drain kidney and haricot beans, place in separate pans and cover with cold water, bring to the boil for 10 minutes then simmer for 1 to 1½ hours until tender. Add a little salt towards the end of the cooking time. Drain and place in a bowl. Cut French beans into 2.5cm (1inch) lengths. Cook the broad beans and French beans in boiling, salted water for 7 to 10 minutes until just tender. Drain and add to the bowl. Pour over the dressing while still warm and mix well. Cool, then stir in the parsley. Transfer to a serving dish.

Suitable for vegetarians   Serves 4

Coleslaw <small>pictured page 75</small>

250g (8oz) white Primo cabbage

1 carrot, peeled and grated

1 onion, peeled and chopped

6 tablespoons mayonnaise (see page 146)

Alternatively use:-

6 tablespoons French dressing (see page 145)

Method

Place all the prepared vegetables in a bowl and mix together. Spoon the chosen dressing over them and mix well with a fork. Serve chilled.

Note.

Coleslaw is great as a filling salad at lunchtime, accompanied by tinned tuna, pilchards or mackerel (in oil or brine). Vegetarians might team it with falafel.

Suitable for vegetarians

Spanakoriso Salad

1kg (2lb) spinach, washed and trimmed

2 large onions, chopped	400ml (15fl.oz) hot water
75ml (3fl. oz) green olive oil	sea salt and pepper
250g (8oz) long grain rice	juice of ½ lemon

Method

Cook the spinach in a little salted water for about 5 minutes until tender. Drain in a colander and press well to extract the moisture.Sauté the onion in the oil until soft but not brown. Chop the spinach and add to the pan with the rice. Stir well until all the grains are covered with oil. Add the hot water and bring to the boil. Reduce the heat to simmer, cover the pan and cook gently until the rice is cooked and all the liquid is absorbed. Season to taste and set to cool. Stir in the lemon juice and chopped herbs and serve at room temperature.

Suitable for vegetarians   Serves 4

MAIN MEALS

Stuffed Marrow (Squash)

1 medium size marrow 1 kg (2lb) approx.

500g savoury mince, precooked (see recipe page 61)

1 clove garlic

sea salt and pepper

Method

Wash and dry the marrow carefully and slice in half longways. Scoop out all the seeds leaving two hollow boat shaped pieces with the flesh still intact. Sprinkle the inside of the two halves with salt and pepper to taste. The mince should be cool enough to handle. Drain off any excess moisture from the mince and compress it in your palms. Fill the marrow 'boats' and press well down. Press the two halves back together tightly and wrap the marrow in foil. Cook in the oven for 40 minute, or until the flesh is soft when stabbed with a fork, at 190°C (375°F) Gas Mark 5. Remove from foil and serve in slices immediately, with a variety of vegetables.

Note.

This recipe can be adapted for vegetarians by using a variety of vegetables bound with cooked rice (and /or nuts if found not to be allergic), as a filling but bear in mind that rice, as a carbohydrate must not be introduced as a main meal until stage 2 unless breakfast is adjusted.

Adaptable for vegetarians   Serves 4

Roast Meat

Suitable roasting cuts are fillet, best end of neck, breast, shoulder, loin and leg.
Roasting times. 35 minutes per ½ kg (1lb) in a moderate oven 180°C (350°F) Gas Mark 4.

Method

Wash the meat and dry with a cloth, place in a roasting tin and rub with sea salt and sprinkle with pepper to taste. Crush a clove of garlic and distribute over the meat, alternatively stab slots into the flesh and place slices of garlic clove in each one. Sprinkle with herbs and add a few knobs of lard or dairy free margarine. Place in the oven for calculated cooking time, (see above).

Roast Fowl

20 minutes per ½ kg (1lb)

Method

Prepare as for roast meat, (see page 54) adding a suitable stuffing if desired.

Lambs Liver with Onions

½ kg (1lb) lambs liver, sliced

2 onions, peeled and finely chopped

1 garlic clove, crushed

1 teaspoon sea salt

a little flour for coating

400ml (¾ pt) stock

oil for frying

pepper

snipped chives for garnish

Method

Heat a little oil in a large frying pan. Add the onion and garlic and fry gently for five minutes until golden. Coat the liver in flour seasoned with pepper to taste and add to the pan. Brown gently on all sides, then gradually stir in the stock. Bring to the boil stirring constantly. Lower the heat and simmer gently for 10 to 15 minutes or until the juices from the liver run pink when pricked with a fork. Serve hot.

Serves 4

Main Meal

Haddock with Cheese and Leek Sauce pictured page 57

500g (1lb) haddock

275ml (½pt) goats, sheeps or soya milk

15g (½oz) dairy free margarine

2 tablespoons plain wholemeal flour

125g (4oz) sheeps milk cheddar cheese (grated)

sea salt and pepper

1 leek, well washed and cut into separated squares

2 lemon slices

sprig of parsley

Method

Place the fish and the milk in a covered skillet pan or fish kettle and poach (simmer gently) for approximately 15 to 20 minutes, depending on the thickness of the fish. Carefully transfer the fish to serving plates and keep hot. Measure 150ml (¼pt) of the fish milk into a jug and discard the rest. Replace the milk into the fish pan and add the leeks, salt and pepper to taste, continue to simmer for a further 5 to 8 minutes. While leeks are cooking, place the margarine in a saucepan on a medium heat and when melted, stir in the flour. Cook for 1 minute. Remove from the heat, and stir in the leek and milk mixture. Add the grated cheese and return to the heat, stirring until sauce thickens. Pour over the fish, garnish with parsley and lemon slices and serve.

Serves 2

Haddock with Cheese and Leek Sauce Recipe page 56

Stir Fry Vegetables Recipe page 59

Stir Fry Vegetables pictured page 58

½ white cabbage, shredded

1 large carrot, sliced in small fingers

1 courgette, (zucchini) sliced

1 red bell pepper, seeded and sliced

1 tin water chestnuts, drained and sliced

2 sticks celery, chopped into 2cm (1inch) pieces

1 root fennel, sliced

sprouted mung beans (if available)

75g (3oz) sugar snap peas   sea salt and pepper

1 tablespoon sesame or olive oil   chopped ginger (if preferred)

Method

Place the oil of choice in a large frying pan or wok and swirl to ensure coating all the sides. Throw in the prepared vegetables and fry gently for about 5 minutes until heated through, but still crisp. Serve immediately.

Note.

Stir frying is a very good way to prepare your vegetables as they retain more of their vitamins when cooked in this way. Almost any vegetables can be used, just as long as they are cut up into small pieces before cooking.

Suitable for vegetarians   Serves 2

Chicken Stir Fry

2 boned chicken breasts, diced

1 clove garlic, crushed   1 teaspoon chopped ginger

4 spring onions, chopped   1 tablespoon of oil for frying

Method

Heat the oil in a frying pan or wok and place all the ingredients together into the oil. Fry over high heat, tossing ingredients until the chicken is cooked, white right through. Add vegetables of choice and stir fry until vegetables are cooked to taste. (see Stir Fry vegetables above). Alternatively serve with a mixed side salad.

Serves 2

Poussins with Herb Sauce

2 tablespoons olive oil

4 x 400g (14oz) poussins (young chickens)

grated rind (prewashed carefully) and juice of 1 lemon

2 tablespoons yeast free chicken stock

2 tablespoons mixed herbs (parsley, chives, thyme, marjoram)

142ml (5fl oz) goats or sheeps yogurt

watercress to garnish

sea salt and pepper

Method

Heat the oil in large pan, add the poussins and brown lightly all over. Add the lemon rind, juice and stock, sea salt and pepper to taste. Cover and simmer for 20 to 25 minutes until tender. Place on a warm serving dish and keep hot. Add herbs and yogurt to the pan. Heat gently whilst stirring, checking the seasoning. Pour sauce around the poussins and garnish with the watercress. Serve.

Serves 4

Fried Chicken in Ginger and Paprika

2 chicken breasts, diced

2 teaspoons chopped ginger

1 clove garlic, crushed

1 teaspoon paprika

oil for frying

Method

Place the oil in a frying pan together with the chicken, ginger and garlic; fry until the chicken turns white. Add the paprika and continue to stir the chicken until it is coated and cooked. Serve hot with salad.

Serves 2

Savoury Mince

500g (1lb) lean minced beef

2 onions, finely chopped

2 carrots, diced

350ml (12fl oz) water

1 teaspoon mixed herbs

2 teaspoons yeast free stock powder

1 tablespoon cornflour

Method

Place the mince in a frying pan over a medium heat and fry until all the fat runs out. Drain the fat off. Transfer the mince into an oven proof casserole dish and add the onions, carrots and herbs. Mix the stock powder and cornflour together and add enough water to mix to a thin paste. Add the rest of the water and stir well to mix. Pour the fluid over the mince and cover with casserole lid. Place in the oven for 1 hour 20 minutes at 190°C (375°F) Gas Mark 5. Serve hot with vegetables of choice.

Note.

Leave savoury meat in the casserole dish and top with potatoes mashed with dairy free margarine and a little of your chosen milk, place back in the oven at the same setting for 20 - 30 minutes and your dish becomes a Shepherds Pie.

Alternatives to beef - T.V.P. (Soya Mince) or Minced Lamb

Serves 4

Scandinavian Mackerel

3 tablespoons lemon juice

300ml (½pt) spring water

1 onion, sliced

1 bay leaf

1 parsley sprig

1 thyme sprig

6 peppercorns

½ teaspoon sea salt

4 mackerel cleaned

Sauce

150g (5oz) yogurt

1 tablespoon dry mustard, mixed

1 tablespoon lemon juice

1 tablespoon chopped fennel

lemon wedges to garnish

Method

Place the 3 tablespoons of lemon juice, water, onion, herbs, peppercorns and salt into a pan. Bring to the boil and simmer for 20 minutes. Place the mackerel in a shallow ovenproof dish and pour the infused liquid over it. Cover and cook in a preheated moderate oven, 180°C (350°F) Gas Mark 4, for 20 to 25 minutes. Transfer the fish to a warm serving dish and keep hot. Put all the sauce ingredients in a small bowl and place over a pan of simmering water. Stir until blended and heated through. Pour sauce over the fish, garnish with lemon wedges and serve immediately.

Serves 4

Trout with Almonds

4 trout, gutted and cleaned with heads on
flour for coating
sea salt and pepper
dairy free margarine for frying
50g (2oz) flaked almonds (if no allergy to them)
4 lemon wedges
parsley to garnish
juice of 1 lemon

Method
Coat the fish in the flour seasoned with salt and pepper. Melt a knob of margarine in a frying pan and add the almonds, frying gently, stirring, for 2-3 minutes or until golden brown. Don't let margarine burn. Remove the almonds with a slotted spoon and drain on kitchen paper. Keep warm. Wipe the pan clean with kitchen paper and add another knob of margarine. When it has melted, add the trout and cook gently for 5 to 8 minutes on each side, or until the trout is tender. Test with a fork; the flesh should flake easily. When cooked, place the fish on a hot serving plate, or on individual dishes, sprinkle with the almonds and lemon juice and garnish with parsley and lemon wedges. Serve immediatley.

Note.
If you cannot tolerate almonds, you can use sunflower seeds as a substitute.

Serves 4

Colombian Turkey

2 x 250g (8oz) turkey breast fillets

25g (1oz) dairy free margarine

sea salt and pepper

2 tablespoons olive oil

1 lemon, halved

Sauce

1 avocado, peeled stoned and cubed

4 spring onions, sliced

½ green bell pepper, cored, seeded and cubed

150ml (5fl oz) goats or sheeps yogurt

To garnish

½ green pepper cored, seeded and sliced into rings

Method

Slice turkey fillets horizontally through with a sharp knife to give 4 thin slices. Place in one layer between 2 sheets of greaseproof paper and beat with a rolling pin or wooden mallet to flatten. Season to taste. Heat the margarine and oil in a pan. Add the fillets, two at a time, and sauté for 2 minutes on each side. Return all fillets to the pan, lower the heat, squeeze the juice from ½ lemon over them and keep warm. To make the sauce, mash the avocado to a paste with juice of other ½ lemon. Add the spring onions, green pepper and salt to taste, then fold in the yogurt. Arrange the turkey on a warmed serving dish and trickle the sauce over it. Garnish with the pepper rings and serve immediately.

Serves 4

VEGETARIAN MAIN MEALS

It is inevitable, if a satisfying vegetarian diet is to be combined with the Candida diet, that a little more carbohydrate will have to be included into the recipes for main meals. This may, for some sufferers, cause the recovery period to become slightly extended. Choose your meals with the greatest care, bearing this in mind and keeping your carbohydrate intake as low as possible.

When extra carbohydrate is present in a recipe, a * is placed against the ingredient as a cautionary measure to help you. If the main meal you are planning for the day has a high carbohydrate content, choose a low carbohydrate breakfast to counterbalance the diet, e.g. yogurt or eggs.

Aduki Bean Crumble

250g (8oz) aduki beans   1 tablespoon olive oil
2 sticks celery, chopped
4 carrots, diced
50g (2oz) sheeps cheese, grated (optional)
*1 tablespoon wholewheat flour
10fl oz (½pt) vegetable stock (approximately)

Topping
*50g (2oz) jumbo oats   sea salt and pepper
*50g (2oz) ordinary oats
3 tablespoons sunflower or sesame oil (according to taste)

Method
Soak beans overnight then cook until soft. Drain. Heat the oil and fry the onions gently, then add the celery and carrots. Fry for a few minutes. Stir in the flour. Add the stock gradually, stirring continuously until a satisfying consistency is achieved. Mix in the beans and place in a casserole dish. Sprinkle cheese on top if being used. Mix the topping together and pile on the top. Bake for 30 minutes 190°C (375°F) Gas Mark 5 until top is slightly brown and crunchy. Serve hot with potatoes and green vegetables.

Serves 4

Parsnip Chips

approx. ½kg (1lb) parsnips, peeled and chipped
sea salt   oil for deep frying

Method
Cook the parsnips in boiling, salted water for about 10-15 minutes, until just tender. Drain and dry thoroughly on a tea towel or kitchen paper. Heat the oil in a chip pan until really hot 190°C (375°F). Place the parsnips into a chip basket and lower into the oil. Fry for 5 minutes or until golden brown. Drain on kitchen paper. Transfer to serving dish. Sprinkle with salt and serve immediately.

Note.
Ordinary potato chips are permitted in the second stage, but these are a pleasant substitute as they are low in carbohydrate.

Spinach and Soft Sheeps Cheese Quiche pictured page 75

900g (2lb) fresh spinach washed and trimmed

30g (1oz) dairy free margarine

250g (8oz) soft sheeps cheese

150ml (5oz) goats, sheeps or soya milk

3 free range eggs, beaten

2 tablespoons grated sheeps cheddar cheese

freshly grated nutmeg

a squeeze of lemon juice

sea salt and pepper

* savoury vegetable suet pastry (see page 142)

Method

Preheat oven to 180°C (350°F) Gas Mark 4

Make up the pastry and line a 25.5cm (10inch) flan dish. Prick the base with a fork and bake for 15 minutes. Remove the flan dish from oven and set aside. Place the spinach in a heavy based saucepan with the margarine and a little salt and pepper, (no need to add water). Cover and cook gently for about 7 minutes, shaking the pan occasionally to prevent sticking, until the spinach becomes soft in the margarine. Drain the spinach, pressing it in a colander to extract excess moisture. Set aside. Place soft cheese in a bowl and beat it, gradually adding milk, then the beaten eggs, salt, pepper and nutmeg. Chop the spinach and stir it into the cheese mixture and pour it into the flan case. Bake for 40 minutes until golden and set. Serve with mixed salad.

Serves 4

Cauliflower Cheese pictured on front cover

1 large cauliflower, divided into florets

15g (½ oz) dairy free margarine

*2 tablespoons plain wholemeal flour

150ml (¼pt) sheeps or soya milk

100g (4oz) sheeps milk cheddar cheese (grated)

sea salt and pepper

Method

Place the cauliflower florets into a pan with boiling salted water and cook for about 10 minutes until just tender, but not too soft. Drain and transfer to a warm ovenproof dish. Melt the margarine in a saucepan and stir in the flour; continue cooking for 1 minute, stirring continuously. Gradually blend in the milk, stirring, until thickened. Reserving about a tablespoon of the grated cheese, stir the rest into the sauce: heat gently until the cheese is melted. Add salt and pepper to taste. Pour the sauce over the cauliflower and sprinkle the reserved cheese on top. Place under a preheated grill until the top is golden brown. Serve hot.

Note.

This works just as well with calabrese (broccoli). For a variation of flavour, 2 teaspoons of dry mustard may be added to the sauce.

Serves 2

Spinach Timbale

700g (1½lb) spinach trimmed and chopped

900fl oz (1½pts) spring water

¾ teaspoon sea salt

50g (2oz) dairy free margarine

1 large onion finely chopped

1 garlic clove crushed

3fl oz (⅛pt) sheeps or goats yogurt

3 eggs lightly beaten

¼ teaspoon white pepper

¼ teaspoon nutmeg (grated)

Method

Place spinach into a saucepan with the water, add the salt. Bring to the boil over a moderate heat, cover and simmer for 7 to 12 minutes or until just tender. Drain spinach through a colander, pressing with a plate to remove excess liquid. Place in a large mixing bowl and set aside. Preheat oven to 180°C (350°F) Gas Mark 4. Lightly grease a medium size mould. Set mould aside. Melt remaining margarine in a frying pan over medium heat. Add onions and garlic, fry until soft (not brown). Add the mixture to the spinach and mix well. Beat the yogurt and eggs together in a mixing bowl, season with salt and pepper to taste. Now add the egg mixture to the spinach mixture and blend well together. Pour the mixture into a mould. Place the mould into a deep roasting tin and surround the mould with boiling water to come half way up the sides of the mould. Place in the oven for 20 to 30 minutes or until the top is risen and set. Serve.

Serves 2

Couscous and Curried Vegetables pictured on front cover

1 head of fennel, trimmed and cut into 1cm (½ inch) pieces

1 red, 1 yellow, 1 geen bell pepper, cored and coarsely chopped

450g (1lb) courgettes (zucchini) cut into 1cm (½ inch) pieces

425g (15oz) chick peas (garbanzos) pre-soaked and cooked (or tinned)

3 carrots, peeled and diced into 1cm (½ inch) squares

2 turnips, peeled and diced into 1cm (½ inch) squares

3 celery stalks, sliced into 1cm (½ inch) pieces

4 teaspoons curry powder (more if desired)

1 large Spanish onion, coarsely chopped

670ml (24fl oz) yeast free stock

*350g (¼lb) couscous   3 tablespoons chopped parsley

425ml (16fl oz) boiling yeast free stock   6 tablespoons lemon juice

1½ tablespoons chopped coriander   4 cloves garlic, minced

Method

Spread the onions in a large frying pan and cook over moderate heat until they are sizzling and sticking to the pan. Stir in 300ml (10fl oz) stock stirring well until it bubbles and the brown deposits in the pan are integrated. Put in all the chopped vegetables the parsley, coriander and curry powder. Stir, then turn down the heat and simmer, stirring frequently until the mixture is thick and the vegetables are "frying" in their own juices. Stir in the remaining stock and the lemon juice, season with sea salt and black pepper to taste. Cover and simmer gently for 15 minutes. Meanwhile bring the 425ml (16fl oz) stock to the boil and remove from heat. Stir in the couscous and allow to steep for 10-15 minutes until the liquid is absorbed. Fluff with a fork. Place the couscous on a large dish and make a hole in the centre. Pour the curried vegetables into the centre and serve immediately

*Extra carbohydrate content; adjust breakfast to counterbalance.

Note.

Just Wholefoods make a good Cous Cous with lentils mix. Available by post. (See Useful Addresses) Page 170

Serves 4

SAUCES

Basic White Sauce

(If avoiding wheat)

250ml (½pt) goats, sheeps or soya milk

15g (½oz) cornflour   30g (1oz) dairy free margarine

Method

Melt the margarine in a saucepan and remove from the heat. Blend in the cornflour. Stir in the milk, return to the heat, bring to the boil then simmer for 2 minutes stirring continuously. Season or flavour to taste.

Note.

This sauce can form the basis for many different flavourings. It can be used as an accompaniment to poached or grilled fish with chopped parsley added. Add cheese and it teams with pasta. Curry powder makes it into an acceptable curry sauce. A little apple concentrate and a vanilla pod (or essence) at the boiling stage will make it into an egg free custard. Cocoa powder makes it into a chocolate sauce. There are endless variations.

Poured into a glass or dessert dish and allowed to cool, this makes an acceptable blancmange for dessert. (Add 1 tablespoon of apple juice only after the first month.)

Suitable for Vegetarians

Basic Cheese Sauce

350ml (12fl oz) goats, sheeps or soya milk

30g (1oz) dairy free margarine   2 tablespoons plain flour

200g (7oz) sheeps milk cheddar cheese, grated.

Method

Melt the margarine in a saucepan and stir in the flour; cook over a low heat for 1 minute stirring continuously, add the milk stirring constantly until sauce thickens. Add the cheese and stir until melted. Serve as complement to all sorts of dishes.

Suitable for Vegetarians

DESSERTS

Carrot Crunch

1 large carrot, peeled and grated

200g (8oz) goats, sheeps or soya yogurt

Method

Grate the carrot on a medium size hole and place in a bowl. Reserve 2 tablespoons of yogurt and mix the rest with the carrot in the bowl. Fill two cocktail glasses with the mixture and spoon the reserved yogurt onto the top. Serve chilled.

Suitable for Vegetarians   Serves 2

Beet Treat

2 medium size cooked beetroot

200g (8oz) goats or sheeps yogurt

Method

Remove the skins from the beetroot and grate on the largest hole on grater; place in a bowl. Reserve two tablespoons of the yogurt. Pour the rest into the bowl with the beetroot. Mix together well. Fill two cocktail glasses with the pink mixture. Top with the plain reserved yogurt. Serve chilled.

Suitable for Vegetarians   Serves 2

Yogurt

Plain live goats, sheeps or soya milk yogurt

Suitable for Vegetarians

SNACKS

Sprouted Seeds and Pulses pictured page 76

All kinds of seeds and pulses can be sprouted with very little trouble and they make delicious and nutritious snacks between meals. Chick peas (garbanzos) and mung beans are particularly tasty. This is how to sprout them.

Take 100g (4oz) chick peas, or mung beans, place them in a glass jar and cover them with cold water to twice their depth. Leave them to soak over night. In the morning they will have swollen to double the size. Drain away the soaking water and rinse them well. Drain them again but don't leave them too dry. Place them on a warm window sill or on a shelf over a radiator. Repeat the rinsing each day until the sprouts start to form (usually 2-3 days). They are now ready to eat.

Note.

If you place the jar in a dark warm place, e.g. the airing cupboard and continue to rinse them daily, the sprouts will continue to grow and they can be used in cooked dishes as extra vegetables.

Shepherds Omelette

2 large free range eggs

sea salt and pepper

50g (2oz) sheeps cheddar cheese

25g (1oz) dairy free margarine

1 tablespoon chopped chives (or chopped spring onion tops)

Method

Preheat the grill. Lightly beat the eggs in a small bowl; add salt and pepper to taste and chives. Cut the cheese into thin slices. Melt the margarine in an 18cm (7inch) frying pan. Make sure the margarine greases the sides of the pan. Pour in the eggs, then quickly place the cheese slices over the top. Cook the base of the omelette for about ½ minute, then transfer the pan, with the omelette in it, under the grill; let the cheese melt, then fold the omelette double to enclose the cheese. Serve and eat immediately.

Suitable for Vegetarians   Serves 1

73

Crudités

Crudités is the French name given to a collection of vegetables, in their raw state, cut into small fingers or bite size pieces, to be eaten with dips. An advantage is that they are quick to prepare and extremely nutritious since none of their value is destroyed by cooking. They are also available, ready prepared from supermarkets. If you don't want to cook, or are caught away from home with nothing suitable to eat, you could purchase some, together with a suitably prepared hummus dip. You need no cutlery and they are quite filling. If you are preparing them at home, here is a list of suitable vegetables to make the best crudités:-

carrots   fennel

celery   peppers

cauliflower   spring onions

cucumber

Suitable for vegetarians

DIPS

Tzatsiki

250g (8oz) Greek sheeps yogurt   ½ cucumber, peeled and grated

2 cloves garlic, crushed   sea salt and pepper

2 teaspoons chopped mint

Method

Grate the cucumber into a bowl using the largest holes in the grater. Drain off excess moisture, then add the yogurt and garlic, salt and pepper to taste. Chill in a refrigerator for 2 hours. Turn into a serving bowl and sprinkle with mint. Serve with crudités. (Yeast free pitta bread after the first month).

Suitable for vegetarians

Dips.

see Hummus page 42

see Baba Ganoush page 46

Coleslaw
Recipe page 53

Crudités
Recipe page 74

Ginger Biscuits
Recipe page 141

Spinach and Cheese Quiche
Recipe page 67

Corn and Potato Stick Snack
Recipe page 125

75

Sprouted Seeds and Pulses Recipe page 73

DRINKS

Mint tea

4 - 6 sprigs fresh mint straight from the plant

500ml (1pt) boiling water

warmed tea pot

Method

Place the sprigs of mint into the pre-warmed pot and pour the boiling water over it. Stir, then leave for about 5 - 7 minutes. Serve.

This tea can also be placed in an airtight jug (without the leaves) and chilled in the refrigerator. It makes a refreshing cool summer drink and can also be transferred into a flask to provide sustenance away from home.

Parsley tea

4 - 6 sprigs fresh parsley

500ml (1pt) boiling water

warmed tea pot

Method

As for mint tea.

Note.

Parsley tea is not only tasty and refreshing but also has helpful properties. It has an extremely beneficial effect on the kidneys, helping to clear infections and it is particularly good for cystitis when drunk in large quantities (1 to 2 litres or 2 to 4 pints daily).

Many herbs and flowers make extremely pleasing drinks, some having health promoting qualities as mentioned above. During the first month of your diet you may try these, but do not use fruit teas until the second stage.

No alcohol is permitted in stage 1

Hot Cocoa

1 to 3 teaspoons of plain cocoa powder (no additives)

1 cup of goats, sheeps or soya milk, boiling hot

Method

Blend the cocoa powder to a paste with a little cold water in the cup and add the boiling water, stirring constantly.

Note.

Do not drink commercially prepared drinking chocolate as it usually includes sugar, milk powder and other additives.

Hot Vegetable Broth

This is a good winter warmer and can be made quickly by placing 1 or 2 teaspoons of bouillon powder in a cup and adding boiling water. Stir and serve.

Camomile tea

Place a handful of dried camomile flowers in a warmed teapot and cover with 500ml (1pt) boiling water. Leave to stand for 5 minutes.

It is possible to buy camomile tea bags in health shops.Camomile is much revered for its soporific (sleep inducing) effects.

STAGE 2

Now you have completed the first month of the programme you will be feeling brighter, and some of the more severe symptoms should have abated, but you still have a long way to go, a further five months. In this stage you can now begin to reintroduce fruit, fruit juices and more carbohydrates, but do so cautiously, one item at a time. It is recommended that for the first week or two you only consume one piece of fruit per day, making it a different type of fruit each time. For example:- Monday, apple - Tuesday, orange - Wednesday, melon - Thursday, pear and so on, gradually increasing your intake as you become confident your symptoms are not returning.

Follow the same pattern with carbohydrates. Monday, introduce potatoes, Tuesday, a rice dish, Wednesday, yeast free bread etc., slowly building on your diet as your system proves capable of tolerating the foods without ill effect. Using this method has a twofold purpose. It allows your system to make the transition smoothly, and it helps you to avoid repetitive eating habits that could lead to your acquiring new food allergies.

If at any time you experience a bad reaction, or a return of old symptoms as you reintroduce the foods, stop eating that food immediately. Make a note to avoid it for a while, and then try reintroducing it later, when your immune system has gained more strength. This may be frustrating, but you will make better progress by showing caution and patience.

For the next 5 months select and plan your meals using the suggestions and recipes in this section, adding them to the first month diet suggestions to give you more choices. The following charts demonstrate how you should proceed.

MEAT EATERS DIET PLAN

	BREAKFAST	LUNCH	DINNER
MONDAY	Kashi (commercially available cereal) with Soya, goats or sheeps milk. Herb tea	Chicken Stew (in a flask if going out) with soda bread	Cold leg of chicken, chips & coleslaw
TUESDAY	Porridge (oats, millet, sorgum) Herb tea	Curried cold rice and diced vegetables goats or sheeps yogurt	Lamb Provencal and vegetables and mashed potatoes
WEDNESDAY	2 Fried eggs with Rösti Potatoes & bacon Herb tea	Stack of yeast free crispbreads with vegetable margarine, goats or sheeps cheese, a tomato, cucumber and carrot	Jacket Potatoes, tinned tuna or mackerel and mixed salad
THURSDAY	Puffed rice (commercially available) with soya, goats or sheeps milk. Herb tea	Salad sandwiches made with yeast free bread and vegetable margarine. Bag of plain crisps. (only salt added)	Turkey steaks with stir fry and Parsnip Chips
FRIDAY	Home made muesli with soya, goats or sheeps milk Herb tea	Hummus & pitta bread with raw cauliflower, carrot, cucumber and celery etc. to dip (crudités)	Beef with Orange casserole and veg and sauté potatoes
SATURDAY	Scrambled eggs on pitta bread Herb tea	Tabbouleh salad or Salmon and Pasta salad	Poached or grilled cod with mashed potatoes, leeks and carrots
SUNDAY	Hearty start or fish cakes Herb tea	Soup of choice with soda bread	Roast chicken (breast), roast potatoes and variety of vegetables. Chocolate Pudding and Sauce

80

VEGETARIAN DIET PLAN

	BREAKFAST	LUNCH	DINNER
MONDAY	Kashi (commercially available cereal) with soya, goats or sheeps milk Herb tea	Leek and Potato soup (in a flask if not at home) with soda bread	Spiced Chick Peas, chips & coleslaw
TUESDAY	Onion Hash Browners Herb tea	Curried cold rice and diced veg goats or sheeps yogurt	Caponata Style Fettucine
WEDNESDAY	2 Fried eggs on pitta bread Herb tea	Stack of yeast free crispbreads with vegetable margarine, goats or sheeps cheese, a tomato, cucumber and carrot	Jacket potatoes, with filling and mixed salad
THURSDAY	Puffed rice (commercially available) with soya, goats or sheeps milk Herb tea	Salad sandwiches made with yeast free bread and vegetable margarine. Bag of crisps	Cheese and Spinach Quiche with stir fry
FRIDAY	Home made muesli with soya, goats or sheeps milk Herb tea	Hummus & pitta bread with raw cauliflower, carrot cucumber and celery to dip (crudites)	Chilli Bean Casserole and rice
SATURDAY	Scambled eggs on pitta bread Herb tea	Tabbouleh salad	Pan Fried Pizza, chips and salad
SUNDAY	Granola Breakfast in a glass	Mexican Stuffed Tomatoes and Tortillas	Mixed Bean Salad and baked potato Chocolate pudding and sauce

BLANK FOR OWN USE

	BREAKFAST	LUNCH	DINNER
MONDAY			
TUESDAY			
WEDNESDAY			
THURSDAY			
FRIDAY			
SATURDAY			
SUNDAY			

BREAKFASTS

Hearty Start

1 tablespoon sunflower or olive oil

¼ bell pepper, chopped

2 tablespoons tomato purée

2 medium tomatoes, chopped

2 sprigs of parsley - scissor snipped

2 sprigs of basil - scissor snipped

*1 slice of lean fresh ham chopped (optional)

1 small onion chopped

sea salt to taste

pepper to taste

2 eggs

Method

Heat oil in a skillet, add onions, pepper, tomatoes, purée and ham. Season with pepper, salt and herbs. Cook uncovered for 10 mins stirring occasionally to stop the mixture sticking. When the juices thicken, break the eggs on top whole. Cover and cook on a low heat until the eggs are poached to your liking, soft, medium or hard. (You can vary the vegetables according to the season and your own particular taste). Serve with or without sauté potatoes depending on the size of your appetite.

Adaptable for Vegetarians (leave out the ham).

Breakfast in a Glass

275ml (½pt) orange juice (freshly squeezed)

1 tablespoon lemon juice

1 tablespoon wheat germ

1 egg

Method

Put all the ingredients together into an electric blender and blend for 30 seconds. Pour into a chilled glass and serve immediately.

Suitable for Vegetarians   Serves 1

Home Made Baked Beans

250g (8oz) haricot beans, soaked overnight

sea salt

For the Sauce

250ml (½pt) goats, sheeps, or soya milk

15g (½oz) cornflour

1 tablespoon tomato purée

1 teaspoon apple concentrate

½ teaspoon sea salt

Method

Drain the beans, place in a saucepan and cover with cold water, bring to the boil and boil rapidly for 10 minutes. Cover and reduce heat. Simmer for about an hour, or until tender, adding a little salt towards the end of the cooking time. Drain and set aside.

Place the cornflour into a small bowl and mix to a thin paste with 2 - 3 tablespoons of milk; add salt and apple concentrate and mix well. Bring the rest of the milk to boil in a saucepan. Remove from the heat and stir in the cornflour mixture, stirring continuously until the sauce thickens. Add the tomato purée and blend in thoroughly. Add the cooked beans and return to a gentle heat stirring continuously until heated through. Serve over yeast free bread or home made pitta (See Breads section pages 132 - 136)

Note

This recipe has been included because it is difficult to find baked beans that do not include sugar, chemical sugar substitutes or preservatives.

Suitable for Vegetarians   Serves 2

Granola

muesli base (see Swiss Style Muesli on page 35)

100g (4oz) dessicated coconut (preservative free)

100g (4oz) dairy free margarine

30g (1oz) 1 tablespoon apple concentrate

Method

Mix muesli and coconut in a bowl. Place the margarine in a pan and heat gently until just melted. Add apple concentrate and mix well. Pour over the dry mixture and mix well. Sprinkle mixture into a roasting tin, and bake in a preheated oven at 190°C (375°F), Gas Mark 5 for about 20 minutes until golden crisp. Stir once or twice during cooking time to avoid burning on top. Leave to cool, then store in an airtight container. Serve as it is or add fresh fruit and yogurt.

Suitable for Vegetarians

Bubble and Squeak

500g (1lb) potatoes cooked and mashed

250g (½lb) cabbage cooked and chopped

25g (1oz) dairy free margarine

sea salt and pepper

Method

Mix the cabbage and potatoes together well adding salt and pepper to taste. Melt the margarine in a 25cm (10inch) frying pan and add the mixture. Fry on high heat until golden brown on bottom, turning several times. Serve hot with a fried egg and a squirt of tomato purée for added flavour.

Suitable for Vegetarians   Serves 2

STARTERS & LUNCHES

Prawn (Shrimp) Apple and Celery Cocktail

1 lettuce, shredded

2 celery sticks, finely chopped

freshly ground black pepper

225g (8oz) peeled prawns or shimps

pinch of paprika to garnish

sea salt

1 dessert apple

juice of 1 lemon

Method

Divide the lettuce equally between 4 glasses and sprinkle lightly with salt. Put the remaining ingredients, except the paprika into a bowl and mix well. Divide the mixture equally between the glasses, sprinkle with paprika and served chilled.

Serves 4

Mexican Stuffed Tomatoes pictured page 97

4 large tomatoes (beefsteak)

1 avocado, peeled and stoned

1 chilli, seeded and chopped

15ml (1 tablespoon) olive oil

½ green bell pepper, seeded and chopped

30ml (2 tablespoons) chopped chives

sea salt and pepper

1 clove garlic, crushed

15ml (1 tablespoon) lime juice

Method

Slice the tops off the tomatoes and scoop out the seeds. Season the insides with salt and pepper. Mash the avocado and mix in the pepper, chives, chilli and garlic. Blend with the lime juice and oil and season to taste. Fill the tomatoes with the avocado mixture and replace the lids. keep cool until time to serve.

Suitable for Vegetarians
Serves 4

86

Ratatouille

1 large aubergine (egg plant)
sea salt
1 large onion, chopped
1 red bell pepper, seeded and sliced
1 green bell pepper, seeded and diced
2 cloves garlic, crushed
45ml (3 tablespoons) olive oil
3 courgettes (zacchini) sliced
450g (1lb) tomatoes, skinned and chopped
30ml (2 tablespoons) chopped fresh basil, marjoram or oregano
6 coriander seeds crushed
sea salt and pepper
1 small bunch of parsley chopped

Method

Slice the aubergine and sprinkle with salt. Leave in colander for about 30 minutes until drained of excess moisture. Rinse well under cold running water and pat dry. Sauté the onions, peppers and garlic in the oil until soft. Add the aubergine (egg plant) and courgettes (zacchini) and cook until golden. Add the tomatoes and herbs and simmer until the sauce is thick and the vegetables are very soft. Add the coriander and seasoning. Cool and sprinkle with chopped parsley. Serve in individual dishes.

Suitable for Vegetarians   Serves 4

SOUPS

Pot - au - feu (French Beef Stew) pictured page 89

1kg (2lb) cubed shin of beef (with bones) excess fat removed

1 teaspoon sea salt

6 peppercorns, finely crushed

1 onion, peeled and stuck with a few cloves

1 bouquet garni

1 garlic clove finely chopped or crushed

2 carrots peeled and quartered

2 celery stalks, scrubbed and chopped

2 leeks, washed and sliced

½kg (1lb) potatoes peeled and diced

fresh chopped parsley to finish

Method

Place the meat and bones in a large saucepan. Cover with water and add salt, bring slowly to the boil. Skim off the scum with a slotted spoon. Lower the heat, add peppercorns, bouquet garni, garlic and onions and cover. Simmer gently for 2 hours or until meat is tender. Skim when necessary. Add more water as needed. Remove the bones and bouquet garni and onion, then add the vegetables. Continue simmering gently for a further 1 hour till both meat and vegetables are well cooked. Before serving, skim once more to remove any fat, adjust seasoning, sprinkle with parsley and serve.

This is a very filling soup and makes a good meal on its own.

Alternative to beef use cubed lamb, chicken or turkey

Serves 4 - 6

Pot -au- feu (French Beef Stew) Recipe page 88

Leek and Potato Soup Recipe page 91

Leek and Potato Soup pictured on page 90

450g (1lb) potatoes, in skins and scrubbed

2 large leeks, washed and chopped

900ml (1½ pt) yeast free stock *

1 tablespoon chopped herbs of choice (optional)

parsley to garnish

Method

Cut the potatoes into 4cm (1inch) cubes and place them together with the chopped leeks, stock and chopped herbs into a large pan with a lid. Bring to the boil and simmer for 10 to 15 minutes until potatoes are cooked. Remove from the heat and pour into a blender a small amount at a time, blending until smooth. Return to the pan and heat through. Pour into serving dishes and garnish with parsley. Serve.

* Yeast free bouillon may be used to make this stock.

Suitable for Vegetarians   Serves 4 to 6

Chilled Avocado Soup

2 ripe avocados

2 teaspoons lemon juice

1 celery stalk, finely chopped

1 tablespoon tomato purée

400g (15oz) goats or sheeps yogurt

sea salt and ground black pepper

400ml (¾pt) chicken stock, skimmed of fat

chopped chives to garnish

Method

Halve the avocados and remove the stone. Scoop out the flesh into a bowl. Add the lemon juice and mash with a fork until smooth. Stir in the remaining ingredients with seasoning to taste, adding enough stock to make a pouring consistency. Chill in the refrigerator for 30 minutes, standing in a bowl of ice cubes. Serve in well chilled bowls and garnish with chopped chives.

Suitable for Vegetarians   Serves 4

New England Fish Chowder

olive oil for frying

1 medium sized onion peeled and chopped

1 garlic clove, crushed with ½ teaspoon sea salt

6 medium tomatoes, skinned and sieved

1 carrot, peeled and chopped

1 celery stalk chopped

¼kg (½lb) potatoes, peeled and diced

½kg (1lb) white fish (cod, haddock, whiting) skinned, filleted and cut
 into bite sized pieces

600ml (1 pint) water

freshly ground black pepper

300ml (½pt) goats, sheeps or soya milk

chopped fresh parsley to garnish

Method

Heat 2 tablespoons of oil in a large fish kettle or saucepan. Add the
vegetables, except the potatoes, and cook gently, stirring occasionally,
for 5 minutes, or until the oil is absorbed into the vegetables. Add the
potatoes, fish and water and bring to the boil slowly, skimming off any
scum that forms with a slotted spoon. Lower the heat, add pepper to
taste, cover the pan and simmer gently for 20 to 30 minutes or until the
fish and vegetables are tender. Be careful not to overcook or they will
disintegrate. Add the milk and reheat gently; adjust the seasoning, stir
in chopped parsley and serve.

Serves 4 to 6

Italian Minestrone Soup

olive oil for frying

100g (4oz) streaky bacon, rinds removed and chopped

1 green bell pepper cored, seeded and finely chopped

1 large onion, peeled and finely chopped

1 garlic clove, crushed with 1 teaspoon salt

3 stalks celery, chopped

6 tomatoes, skins removed

2 medium size carrots, peeled and finely chopped

2 courgettes (zacchuni), finely chopped

100g (4oz) pasta shapes

freshly ground black pepper

1 teaspoon dried oregano or basil

1 tablespoon tomato purée

1½ litre (2½pts) chicken stock, skimmed of fat

450g (1lb) red kidney beans, soaked and cooked

Method

Heat 2 tablespoons of olive oil in a large saucepan. Add the bacon, pepper, onion and garlic and fry gently for 5 to 10 minutes, or until the onions are golden and the bacon is crisp. Stir the rest of the vegetables, (except the kidney beans) and the pasta, into the pan. Add the pepper and stir in the oregano or basil, tomato purée and stock. Bring to the boil and simmer gently for 20 minutes, stirring occasionally. Add the kidney beans and simmer for 10 minutes or until all the vegetables are tender.

Adjust seasoning and serve hot with yeast free garlic bread.

Serves 4 to 6

French Onion Soup

3 Spanish onions, peeled and sliced into rings

knob of dairy free margarine for frying

*1¼ litre (2pt) yeast free home made beef stock, skimmed of fat

freshly ground black pepper   sea salt

2 tablespoons flour

To finish:

4 slices of yeast free bread, spread with dairy free margarine

4 large slices of sheeps Cheddar cheese

Method

Put the marg, in a saucepan. Add the onions and fry gently until soft and golden. Stir in the flour and cook gently for a further 2 minutes, stirring constantly. Gradually stir in the stock and bring to the boil. Season to taste, then lower the heat and simmer for 20 to 25 minutes. Pour the soup into individual warm bowls and float a slice of bread on each. Top with a slice of cheese and sprinkle with the black pepper. Place under a preheated grill for about 5 minutes or until the cheese melts. Serve immediately.

Adjustable for Vegetarians   Serves 4

* Vegetarians use vegetable stock

Avgolemono Soup from Cyprus

1¼ litres (2pt) chicken stock, skimmed of fat

50g (2oz) long grain brown rice

juice of 1 - 2 lemons (approx 90ml or 3fl oz)

2 eggs   freshly ground black pepper

sea salt   scissor snipped chives to garnish

Method

Put the stock and rice in a saucepan. Bring to the boil, stir once and cover, then lower heat and simmer gently for 20 minutes. Beat the lemon juice and eggs together in a bowl then beat in a few spoonfuls of the hot stock. Blend into the remaining stock and rice and reheat very gently. **Do not allow soup to boil or it will curdle.** Adjust seasoning to taste. Serve immediatley sprinkled with the chives.

Serves 4

SALADS

Special Potato Salad

450g (1lb) new potatoes

pinch of sea salt

4 rashers back bacon (optional) (vegetarians try chopped red onion)

bunch spring onions, chopped

Dressing

2 tablespoons lemon juice

3 tablespoons olive oil

1 teaspoon dry mustard

1 tablespoon chopped fresh mint

Method

Cook the potatoes in boiling salted water for 15 minutes; drain. Meanwhile, cook the bacon under a hot grill until crisp and put in a bowl with the spring onions and hot potatoes. Put dressing ingredients all together in a screw topped jar and shake well. Pour over potato salad, toss and serve.

Adjustable for Vegetarians   Serves 4

Exotic Duck Salad

1 roasted 2kg (4½lb) duckling

2 red dessert apples, cored and diced

50g (2oz) chopped fresh walnuts (for those avoiding nuts, substitute pumpkin seeds)

2 kiwi fruit, peeled and sliced

2 heads of chicory, separated into leaves

1 bunch watercress, washed and trimmed

Dressing

60ml (4 tablepoons) mayonnaise (see page 146)

5ml (1 teaspoon) chopped capers

15ml (1 tablespoon) chopped courgette (zacchini)

10ml (2 teaspoons) dry mustard

15ml (1 tablespoon) chopped parsley

juice of ½ lemon

Method

Strip skin from duckling and cook it under a hot grill until really crisp and golden brown. Remove the duckling meat from the bones and cut into small chunks. Mix with the walnuts and apple in a bowl. Make up the dressing by blending together in a screw topped jar, and pour over the duck salad ingredients. Toss well. Arrange chicory leaves, watercress and kiwi slices around a large flat dish to form a colourful border design. Place the duck salad in the centre and crumble the crisp skin on top. Serve.

Note.   Serves 4

This recipe works just as well with chicken and turkey.

Mexican Stuffed Tomatoes
Recipe page 86

Cauliflower and Apple Crunch
Recipe page 99

Sprouted Seeds and Pulses
Recipe page 73

Beef and Green Rice Salad
Recipe page 101

Swiss Rösti Potatoes
Recipe page 36

Tabouleh Recipe page 99

Cauliflower and Apple Crunch pictured page 97

1 small cauliflower, divided into florets

3 sticks celery chopped

2 small red dessert apples, cored and diced

100g (4oz) pine kernels

juice of 1 orange

150ml (¼pt) goats or sheeps yogurt

30ml (2 tablespoons) chopped parsley

Method

Mix the cauliflower, celery, apple and pine kernels all together in a bowl. Blend the yogurt and orange juice. Add seasoning. Toss the yogurt and salad mixture together gently and sprinkle with parsley. Serve chilled.

Suitable for Vegetarians   Serves 4

Tabbouleh pictured page 98

75g (3oz) bulgar wheat

1 teacup chopped parsley

3 tablespoons chopped mint

4 spring onions chopped finely

½ cucumber, diced

2 tablespoons olive oil

juice of 1 lemon

sea salt and pepper

Method

Soak the bulgar wheat in cold water for 1 hour. Line a sieve with muslin and tip wheat into it. Lift out the muslin and squeeze out as much moisture as possible. Place the wheat in a bowl and add remaining ingredients, season with sea salt and pepper to taste. Toss thoroughly, then transfer to a shallow serving dish.

Suitable for Vegetarians   Serves 4

Zesty Courgette (Zacchini) and Chick Pea (Garbanzo) Salad

3 medium courgettes about 165g (6oz) each

½ teaspoon sea salt

75ml (5 tablespoons) lemon juice

1 clove garlic (crushed)

¼ teaspoon dried, crushed thyme leaves

125ml olive oil

200g (250ml) chick peas, presoaked and cooked

3 onions, finely chopped

1 ripe avocado, stoned, peeled and cut into 1.5cm (½ inch) cubes

120g (4oz) crumbled sheeps feta cheese

1 lettuce, separated into individual leaves, washed and drained

1 sliced tomato

1 sprig parsley to garnish

Method

Cut courgettes lengthwise into halves; cut halves crosswise into 6mm (½inch) slices. Place slices in bowl; sprinkle with salt. Toss to mix. Spread on several layers of paper towels to drain for 30 minutes.

Combine lemon juice, garlic and thyme in a bowl. Gradually add the olive oil, whisking continuously until dressing is thoroughly blended. Pat zacchini dry and add to the dressing. Add chick peas, and onions, toss lightly to coat. Cover and refrigerate for at least 30 minutes or up to 4 hours, stirring occasionally. Add avocado and cheese just before serving; toss lightly to mix.

Serve salad in a lettuce lined shallow bowl. Garnish with slices of tomato and a sprig of parsley.

You can use sliced radishes in season adding them at the same time as the avocado and cheese.

Note.

This salad, not only looks good, but it tastes marvellous. Great for entertaining.

Suitable for Vegetarians   Serves 4

Beef and Green Rice Salad pictured page 97

100g (4oz) brown rice

3 tablespoons olive oil

2 teaspoons lemon juice

sea salt and pepper

2 tablespoons chopped parsley

2 tablespoons chopped chives

1 tablespoon chopped dill

1 tablespoon chopped taragon

½ small cucumber, diced

25g (1oz) pumpkin seeds

1 green bell pepper, deseeded and diced

500g (2lb) cold, lean roast beef, cut into slices
approx 10cm (4inch) x 8cm (3inch)

Method

Cook the rice and drain it well. While still warm, stir in the oil, lemon juice and seasoning. When cool, stir in all other ingredients. Test seasoning and adjust if necessary. Chill slightly. Arrange the beef slices around the edge of a flat plate or serving dish and pile the rice salad in the centre. Serve.

For alternative to beef use - Cold roast lamb, chicken or turkey

Salmon and Pasta Salad

350g (12oz) linguine or tagliatelle

60ml (4 tablespoons) olive oil

juice of half a lemon

sea salt and pepper

250g (8oz) shelled cooked prawns

250g (8oz) fresh salmon, skinned and boned

45ml (3 tablespoons) chopped parsley and tarragon

Method

Cook the pasta in boiling salted water until tender. Drain and mix in the oil to prevent the strands sticking together. Cut the salmon into large chunks and lightly poach or steam. Mix with the pasta and add the prawns. Blend the oil, lemon and seasoning and gently toss the salad in the dressing. Sprinkle with herbs.

Serves 4

MAIN MEALS

Beef with Orange

1½ tablespoons plain wholemeal flour

sea salt and pepper

350g (12oz) chuck steak, cubed

15g (½oz) dairy free margarine

1 small chopped onion

grated orange rind

200ml (⅓pt) yeast free stock

juice of 2 small oranges

½ green bell pepper, chopped

chopped parsley to garnish

Method

Season the flour with salt and pepper and use to coat the meat. Melt the margarine into a pan, add the onion and bell pepper and fry, turning, until evenly browned. Transfer to a 900ml (1½pt) casserole dish. Stir in the orange rind and juice, stock and salt and pepper to taste. Cover and cook in a preheated oven 160°C (325°F) Gas Mark 3 for 1 to 1¼ hours. Serve hot garnished with the parsley.

Beef Alternatives - Pork or Lamb

Serves 4

Guinea Fowl with Raspberries

1 oven ready guinea fowl

25g (1oz) dairy free margarine

175g (6oz) fresh raspberries

4 tablespoons goats or sheeps yogurt

sea salt and pepper

2 rosemary sprigs

1 tablespoon olive oil

4 tablespoons lemon juice

50g (2oz) fresh raspberries, parsley sprigs and bay leaves to garnish

Method

Season the guinea fowl well, inside and out. Place ½ the margarine, the rosemary and 50g (2oz) of the raspberries in the body cavity. Heat the remaining margarine and oil in a pan, add the guinea fowl and brown on all sides. Add the lemon juice. Lay the guinea fowl on its side and cook for 20 to 25 minutes, then turn onto the other side and cook for a further 20 to 25 minutes. Transfer to a warm serving dish; keep warm. Add the yogurt, salt and pepper to taste to the pan, stirring well to disolve the sediment, then add the remaining raspberries and heat through without stirring. Do not boil. Spoon the raspberry sauce around the guine fowl. Garnish with raspberries and herbs and serve immediately.

Serves 4

Lasagne

25g (1oz) dairy free margarine	1 large onion, peeled & chopped
400g (15g) can chopped tomatoes	2 teaspoons tomato purée
1 clove garlic, crushed	sea salt and pepper
2 teaspoons cornflour	150g (6oz) lasagne
*250g (8oz) minced beef	25g (1oz) flour

150ml (¼pt) beef stock (vegetable stock)
1 teaspoon chopped fresh marjoram - dried if fresh unavailable
1 teaspoon chopped fresh basil - dried if fresh unavailable
300ml (½pt) goats, sheeps or soya milk
65g (2½oz) sheeps Cheddar cheese, grated

Method

Heat the margarine and fry onions until soft. Stir in the minced beef and cook until lightly browned. Add tomatoes, purée, stock, herbs and garlic. Season well, cover and simmer for 30 minutes. Blend cornflour with cold water, and stir into the sauce. Bring to the boil stirring. Cook the lasagne in boiling, salted water for 10 - 15 minutes. Drain and refresh in cold water. For coating sauce, heat the margarine and stir in the flour, cooking for 2 minutes. Allow to cool, then slowly add the milk. Return to heat and bring to the boil stirring constantly. Stir in the cheese. Cover the base of an oiled ovenproof dish with half the lasagne. Spoon half the meat sauce over it, now add another layer of pasta, followed by the rest of the meat sauce.* Top with the cheese sauce. Sprinkle with a little more grated cheese and place in a moderate oven for 30 to 35 minutes until top is slightly browned. 190°C (375°F) Gas Mark 5.

* To adapt for vegetarian version, replace meat with diced mixed vegetables, adding at the same time as stock and herbs etc..... Replace beef stock with vegetable stock.

Note.

To save on cooking time, you could make up the lasagne in individual dishes and, after allowing to cool thoroughly, wrap and freeze. They can then be reheated and used when you are busy or too tired to cook.

Alternative to beef - use T.V.P. (Soya Mince) or minced lamb.

Adaptable for Vegetarians   Serves 4 - 5

Moussaka

2 medium aubergines (egg plants), sliced

sea salt and pepper

6 tablespoons olive oil (approximately)

1 large onion, chopped

1 clove garlic, finely chopped

750g (1½lb) cooked lamb, finely chopped or minced

250g (8oz) tomatoes, skinned and chopped

2 tablespoons chopped parsley

grated nutmeg

25g (1oz) dairy free margarine

25g (1oz) plain wholemeal flour

300ml (½pt) goats, sheeps or soya milk

1 egg yolk

parsley sprigs to garnish

Method

Sprinkle the aubergine slices with salt and leave to drain for 30 mins. Rinse and pat dry. Heat a little of the oil in a frying pan. Fry aubergine slices until golden brown, adding more oil as needed. Set aside. Put the garlic and onion in the pan with more oil if necessary, and fry until softened. Stir in the lamb, tomatoes, chopped parsley, salt, pepper and nutmeg to taste. Cook for 5 mins. Make alternative layers of aubergine and lamb in a casserole, beginning and ending with aubergine. Melt the margarine in a saucepan, add the flour and cook, stirring, for 1 minute. Gradually stir in the milk and bring to the boil. Simmer, stirring, until thickened. Season with salt, pepper and nutmeg to taste. Cool slightly, then beat in the egg yolk. Pour sauce over the top and cook in a preheated moderate oven 180°C (350°F), Gas Mark 4 for 45 minutes. Garnish with parsley, serve.

Serves 4

Fish Boulangére

500g (1lb) potatoes   sea salt and pepper
50g (2oz) dairy, free margarine   1 large onion, thinly sliced
1 clove of garlic, crushed or finely chopped
750g (1½lb) white fish fillets, skinned and cut into chunks

Method

Par-cook potatoes in boiling, salted water for 10 mins. Drain and slice thinly. Cream half the margarine with the crushed garlic and spread over the bottom of a casserole. Arrange fish chunks on top and sprinkle with sea salt and pepper to taste. Cover with slices of onion and then add the slices of potato. Dot the top with the rest of the margarine. Cook in a preheated moderate oven, 180°C (350°F) Gas Mark 4 for about 40 mins, or until the potatoes are tender and nicely browned.

Note.

Don't throw your potato peelings away. Spread them on a baking tray and place them in the oven at 200°C (400°F) Gas Mark 6 for about 30 minutes until they are all brown and crunchy, they make a nutritious and tasty snack.

Serves 4

Plate Pizza pictured page 108

2 tablespoons tomato purée   1 small onion, chopped
1 tomato, deseeded and chopped   * 1oz chopped ham (optional)
yeast free bread base (see Pizza Base - page 136)
100g (4oz) sheeps Cheddar cheese, grated
¼ green bell pepper, deseeded & chopped, or 5cm (2inch) courgette, diced
½ teaspoon fresh chopped oregano or dried mixed herbs
25.5cm (10inch) oven proof plate

Method

Make up the base and place on the plate. Spread tomato purée over the base, sprinkle the onion over; scatter cheese evenly over and spread tomato, pepper or courgette and ham on the top. Finish with herbs. Place in the oven at 200°C (400°F) Gas Mark 6 for 15 - 20 minutes. Serve with mixed salad. Vary topping to suit taste, but keep the rules

*Adaptable for Vegetarians (Leave off the ham)   Serves 1 - 4

Lamb Provencal pictured page 107

500g (1lb) lean, boned, leg of lamb
2 tablespoons olive oil
1 large onion, sliced
1 garlic clove, crushed
6 skinned tomatoes, chopped
1 tablespoon tomato purée
150ml (¼pt) water
1 rosemary sprig
1 thyme sprig
1 bay leaf
sea salt and freshly ground black pepper
1 green (bell) pepper cored, seeded and sliced
1 courgette (zacchini) diced
chopped parsley to garnish

Method

Trim any excess fat from the lamb and cut into 2.5cm (1inch) squares. Heat the oil in a flameproof casserole or heavy based pan. Add the onion and garlic and sauté until golden. Add the lamb and cook for 5 minutes stirring frequently until evenly browned. Stir in the tomatoes and their juice, tomato purée and water. Add the herbs, salt and pepper to taste. Stir well then cover and simmer for 45 minutes. Add the courgettes (zacchini) and bell pepper now, continue to simmer for a further 20 minutes. Discard herbs, sprinkle with the chopped parsley and serve with brown rice.

Serves 4

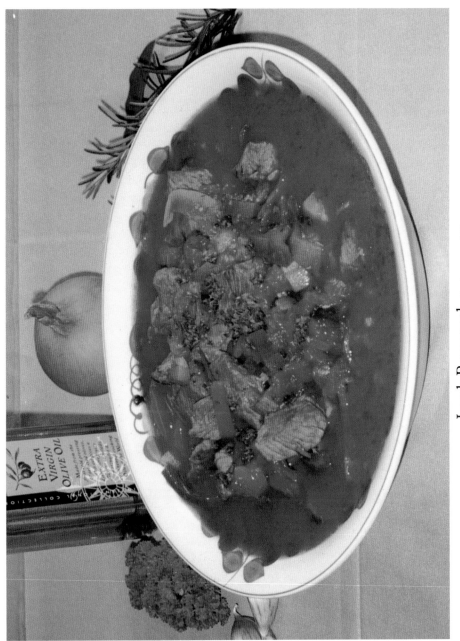

Lamb Provencal Recipe page 106

Plate Pizza Recipe page 105

Pan Fried Pizza

225g (8oz) self raising flour 85% wheatmeal 15% white unbleached
4 tablespoons tomato purée
400g (14oz) tin Italian chopped tomatoes
150g (5oz) hard sheeps cheddar cheese, grated
1 finely chopped onion
1 teaspoon oregano
* 45g (1¾oz) tin anchovy fillets, drained & cut in half lengthwise
½ teaspoon sea salt
pepper
4 - 5 tablespoons olive oil

Method

Sieve flour, salt, pepper and oregano into a bowl, make a well in the middle and pour in 2 tablespoons of olive oil, then 4 tablespoons of water. Mix to a soft dough, add more water if necessary. Turn dough onto a floured surface and knead lightly. Roll out a round shape to fit the base of a 23-25cm (9 or 10 inch) frying pan. Heat 1 tablespoon olive oil in pan, place round of dough into pan and cook over low heat for 5 minutes until base is slightly brown. Oil a plate and turn the base onto it thus turning it upside down. Replace the base to the pan and cook the other side. While the second side is cooking spread tomato purée on top, then the tomatoes, next the onion and cover with grated cheese and sprinkle with oregano. Distribute anchovy fillets evenly or forming a pattern on top. Check if underside is done and transfer the pan to a preheated grill for 2 - 3 minutes to melt the cheese and warm the topping. Serve with mixed salad.

Note.
Vary topping to suit taste but keep the rules.

* Adjustable for Vegetarians (Leave off the anchovies)   Serves 2 - 4

Mediterranean Fish Stew

3 tablespoons olive oil

2 onions, sliced

2 cloves garlic, crushed

4 large tomatoes, skinned and chopped

150ml (¼pt) water

150ml (¼pt) fresh lemon juice

1 bay leaf

1 teaspoon sea salt

½ teaspoon black pepper

750g (1½lb) cod fillet, skinned and boned

600ml (1pt) mussels

175g (6oz) frozen or fresh peeled prawns (if frozen, thawed)

1 tablespoon chopped parsley

Method

Heat oil in a pan, add the onions and fry until softened. Add the garlic, tomatoes, half the water, the lemon juice, bay leaf, salt and pepper. Simmer for 15 minutes. Cut the cod into 5cm (2inch) squares, add to the pan and simmer for 15 minutes. Scrub the mussels thoroughly pulling off the beard. Discard any which are open and will not close when tapped. Put them into a heavy pan with the remaining water, cover and cook over high heat for 5 minutes until they have opened; discard any that do not.

Discard the top shell from each mussel. Add the mussels with their liquid and the prawns to the stew, cook for a further 3 minutes. Turn into a warm serving dish and sprinkle with parsley. Serve immediately with yeast free crusty bread toasted and spread with garlic butter. (see page 135)

Serves 4

VEGETARIAN MAIN MEALS

Spanish Omelette

2 fresh, free range eggs

1 small precooked potato, chopped into very small pieces (or grated)

1 tablespoon onion, finely chopped

1 tablespoon chives, finely chopped (optional)

sea salt and pepper

1 tablespoon olive oil

1 tablespoon goats, sheeps or soya milk

Method

Beat the egg and milk together in a small bowl. Heat the oil in an 18cm (7inch) omelette pan. Pour the egg mixture into the pan and add the potato, onion and chives, salt and pepper as quickly as possible. Allow to cook over a slow heat for approximately 4 minutes or until the egg is set and the underside is slightly browned. Flip over and cook the other side. Slide out onto a plate and serve hot with a green salad.

Serves 1

Caponata - Style Fetuccine

1 aubergine (eggplant)

1½ teaspoons sea salt

3 medium tomatoes

3 tablespoons olive oil

1 small green bell pepper, cored and sliced

1 medium onion, coarsely chopped

2 cloves garlic, crushed

2 tablespoons capers

1 small courgette (zucchini) diced

¼ teaspoon each, ground cinnamon and black pepper

250g (8oz) fresh spinach fetuccine, hot cooked and drained

fresh basil leaves to garnish

Method

Cut aubergine into 6mm (¼inch) slices and place in a colander. Sprinkle with 1 teaspoon of salt. Leave to drain for 1 hour. Meanwhile cut the tomatoes in half and remove seeds; discard. Coarsely chop. Move oven rack to lowest position. Preheat oven to 230°C (450°F) Gas Mark 7. Place aubergine slices on a baking sheet and brush both sides with some of the oil. Bake for 10 minutes or until lightly browned. Turn and repeat on the other side. Set aside.

Heat remaining oil in a large frying pan over medium heat. Cook bell peppers in pan until they turn bright green (about 5 minutes). Transfer to a plate and set aside. Add onion and garlic to the same pan, cook and stir for 5 minutes until onion is soft. Add tomatoes, courgettes, capers, cinnamon and black pepper and remaining ¼ teaspoon salt. Cook until most of the liquid is evaporated. Cut roasted aubergine into quarters; add tomato mixture and the reserved bell pepper; heat through. Serve over fettucine. Garnish with basil leaves.

Serves 2

Vegetable Curry

100g (4oz) dessicated coconut (preservative free)

250ml (½pt) goats, sheeps or soya milk

1 onion, chopped finely

1 garlic clove, crushed

30g (1oz) root ginger, chopped finely

140g (5oz) dairy free margarine

2 level tablespoons curry powder

45g (1½oz) wholemeal flour

500ml (1pt) vegetable stock

sea salt and pepper

140g (5oz) goats or sheeps yogurt

675g (1½lb) diced mixed vegetables

3 tablespoons lemon juice

Method

Place the coconut and milk in a pan and bring to the boil; simmer for 2 minutes. Strain the milk into a bowl and set aside. Melt the margarine in a pan and fry the onion, garlic and ginger until onion is soft but not brown. Add the curry powder and add flour and cook stirring continuously for 1 minute. Gradually blend in the coconut milk, stock and seasoning. Bring to the boil and simmer, stirring continuously for 3 - 4 minutes. Add the diced vegetables and stir. Cook gently for 15 - 20 minutes until vegetables are tender. Stir in the lemon juice a little at a time. Blend in the yogurt and reheat **taking care not to let it boil.** Serve at once with long grain brown rice.

Serves 2

Chilli Bean Casserole

250g (½lb) red kidney beans

1¼ litres (2pts) water for soaking

1¼ litres (2pts) water for boiling

1 tablespoon virgin olive oil

250g (½lb) onions, peeled and finely chopped

1 clove garlic, crushed

250g (½lb) mixed vegetables of choice, cubed 1cm (½inch) pieces

½ teaspoon dried or fresh basil (chopped)

1 teaspoon ground cumin

¼ teaspoon chilli powder (or 1 fresh chilli, seeded and finely chopped)

6 tomatoes skinned and chopped

2 tablespoons tomato purée

4 tablespoons fresh lemon juice

50g (2oz) bulgar wheat

sea salt and pepper

Method

Drain the soaked beans, rinse thoroughly in running water and place in a pan with 1¼ litres (2pt) water. Bring to the boil and boil for 10 minutes. Reduce heat, partially cover, and simmer for a further 30 minutes or until beans are tender. Remove from heat, drain, but retain the stock. Heat oil in a large pan and fry the onions and garlic for a few minutes until onions are soft. Add the chopped vegetables, beans, basil and spices. Stir well and cook for 5 minutes. Add the tomatoes, purée, lemon juice, bulgar wheat and ½ litre (1pt) of the stock. Bring to the boil. Transfer into a casserole dish, cover and cook in oven for 50 to 60 minutes 180°C (350°F) Gas Mark 4. Season to taste and serve together with jacket potatoes and lightly steamed green vegetables.

Serves 4

Spiced Chick Peas (Garbanzos) pictured on front cover

175g (6oz) chick peas (garbanzos)

3 pints water for soaking

3 pints water for cooking

2 tablespoons virgin olive oil

2 medium onions, peeled and chopped

½ teaspoonful chilli powder

1 teaspoon ground coriander

1 teaspoon grated root ginger

1 teaspoon ground cumin

1 red bell pepper, seeded and chopped

1 green bell pepper, seeded and chopped

4 tablespoons tomato purée

10fl oz (½pt) yeast free vegetable stock

juice of 1 lemon

Method

Drain presoaked peas and rinse thoroughly with fresh water. Place in a large pan and cover with 1½ litres (3pts) fresh water, bring to the boil and boil for 10 minutes. Scoop off and discard any scum that may form. Reduce heat and simmer for a further 30 minutes, or until peas are soft. Drain. Heat the oil in a large pan and gently fry the onions together with the spices for 5 - 7 minutes, until the onions are soft but not brown. Add the peppers and chick peas. Dissolve the tomato purée in the stock and add to the pan. Cook for 10 minutes and then add the lemon juice and seasoning to taste. Remove from the heat and stir well. Serve with long grain brown rice and side salad.

Serves 4

Jacket Potatoes

2 large, sound, potatoes, scrubbed well and stabbed all round with a fork.

Method

If crispy skins are wanted, then place the potatoes, just as they are on to a baking tray and bake for 1½ hours, approximately, depending on size of the potatoes, at 190°C (375°F) Gas Mark 5.

If softer skins are required, wrap in tinfoil before placing in the oven.

Suggested Fillings

Home-made baked beans

Hummus or tzatziki dip over chopped onions and chunks of cucumber

Coleslaw

Grated hard goats or sheeps cheese

For mayonnaise recipe see page 146
With a mixed salad this can form a wonderfully nutritious meal. Great when you come in from the cold.

Note.

Meat eaters may choose to use this recipe, adding prawns in seafood sauce or tuna with mayonnaise and chopped cucumber.

Both vegetarians and meat eaters can dream up their own fillings, the scope is endless.

Serves 2

Stuffed Kohlrabi (or Turnips)

4 kohlrabi each about 6.25cm (2½inch) in diameter

2 tablespoons oil

1 small onion, chopped

¼ teaspoon dry mustard

¼ teaspoon caraway seeds

2 slices pumpernickel, crumbled

1 cob of corn, cooked and kernels removed from cob

2 tablespoons mayonnaise (see page146)

30g (1oz) crumbled sheeps feta cheese

Method

Detach 1 leaf from kohlrabi, chop and set aside. Cut off slice from bottom of each kohlrabi and cut off and discard stems. Peel each kohlrabi vertically from top to bottom. Hollow out the centres with a melon baller, leaving 6mm (¼inch) thick shells; reserve the pulp. Fill large saucepan with water enough to cover the kohlrabies. Bring to the boil; add the kohlrabi shells. Boil for 15 minutes or until crisp-tender. Remove shells with a slotted spoon; drain upside down on paper towels. Chop reserved pulp. Heat oil in small frying pan. Add pulp, onion, mustard and caraway seeds; cook, stirring until onion is soft. Stir in breadcrumbs and corn kernels; stir in reserve kohlrabi leaf, mayonnaise and cheese. Fill the shells with the crumb mixture. Place remaining mixture in oiled baking dish; place kohlrabies in the dish and bake in a preheated oven uncovered for 20 minutes until kohlrabies are heated through and fork tender. 180°C (350°F) Gas Mark 4. Serve immediately with additional filling around. Garnish with a sprig of raspberry leaf if desired.

Note.

Kohlrabi means "cabbage turnip" and its bulb tastes like a broccoli stem. The leaves taste like kale or spinach. If kohlrabi is not readily available in your area, this recipe works well with English turnips.

Serves 4 as starter; Serves 1 as main dish

DESSERTS

Yogurt Ice Cream

400g (16fl oz) Greek sheeps milk yogurt

4 tablespoons apple concentrate   4 egg whites

Method

Separate eggs carefully making sure none of the yolk gets into the whites. Place the egg whites into a bowl and whisk until they form peaks and are stiff. Whisk the yogurt and apple concentrate together until the mixture is thick and creamy. Add the flavourings at this stage if desired (see note below). Fold in the whisked egg whites and place in the refrigerator until frozen. Usually about 3 hours. Remove and stand for 5 minutes. Serve.

Note.

Flavourings that may be added:-

2 teaspoons vanilla essence	vanilla ice cream
2 teaspoons lemon essence	lemon ice cream
2 teaspoons peppermint oil	peppermint ice cream
2 tablespoons cocoa powder	chocolate ice cream
2 teaspoons orange essence	orange ice cream

Suitable for Vegetarians Makes approximately 900ml (1½pts) 4 cups

Soya Ice Cream

550ml (1pt) concentrated soya milk (Health Stores)

2 tablespoons apple concentrate

4 drops vanilla essence

2 teaspoons agar agar

Method

Beat the milk, apple concentrate and vanilla essence together. Add the agar agar and mix well. Heat in a saucepan to boiling point. Boil, stirring continuously for 2 mins. Transfer to a bowl and allow to cool. Beat again and place in a freezer proof container. Place in freezer compartment in refrigerator for approximately 4 hours. Remove 5 - 10 minutes before serving.

Suitable for Vegetarians   Makes approximately 550ml (1pt)

Fresh Fruit Salad

2 tablespoons apple concentrate

120ml (4fl oz) water

thinly pared rind and juice of 1 lemon

1 green dessert apple, quartered and cored

1 pear, quartered and cored

1 banana, sliced

1 small pineapple, peeled, cored and cubed

2 tangarines or clementines, divided into segments

4oz strawberries, sliced

1 kiwi fruit, peeled and sliced across

Method

Place the water, lemon rind and apple concentrate in a small saucepan and bring to the boil. Simmer for 2 minutes, then remove the lemon rind and leave to cool. Stir in the lemon juice. Slice the apple, pear and banana into a bowl and pour the lemon syrup over the fruit, making sure it is well coated. Peel the pineapple and cut the flesh into cubes, discarding the central core. Peel the tangerines or clementines, (carefully discarding the pith and pips) dividing them into segments. Add all the remaining fruit to the bowl and mix gently. Turn into a glass serving dish and chill until use.

Serve with Yogurt Snow (See page 121)

Note.
Many Candida sufferers find that they cannot tolerate strawberries, if this is true of you, leave them out and add a little colour by substituting firm, stoned and halved red plums.

Suitable for Vegetarians   Serves 4

Spicy Surprise

110g (4oz) brown rice flour

125ml (5fl oz) oil of choice

2 teaspoons baking powder

2 medium size carrots (grated)

1 teaspoon ground ginger

2 heaped teaspoons mixed spice

2 teaspoons vanilla essence

Method

Beat all ingredients together and place mixture in a greased tin (preferably with a removable bottom). Cook in a medium oven 180°C (350°F) Gas Mark 4 for about 20 mins, until risen and golden brown. Serve hot or cold.

This is delicious served hot with melted dairy free margarine or yogurt ice cream.

Suitable for Vegetarians   Serves 2

Apple and Pear Crumble

250g (8oz) apples peeled, cored and sliced

250g (8oz) pears peeled, cored and sliced

grated rind of 1 well scrubbed lemon

1/4 teaspoon ground cinnamon

1 tablespoon water

75g (3oz) Swiss style muesli (see page 35)

30g (1oz) porridge oats

Method

Place the apples and pears in a pan with the lemon rind, cinnamon and water. Cook gently until the fruit is soft, but not pulpy. Spoon into a 1.2 litre (2pt) ovenproof dish. Mix together the muesli and oats and pile on top of the fruit. Cook in a preheated oven on 190°C (375°F) Gas Mark 5 for 15 minutes or until topping is crisp. Serve hot or cold.

Suitable for Vegetarians   Serves 4

Minted Apple Snow pictured on front cover

1kg (2lbs) cooking apples, peeled, cored and sliced

finely grated rind and juice of 1 orange

3 tablespoons apple concentrate

4 large mint sprigs

2 egg whites

Method

Put the apples in a pan and add the orange rind, juice and apple concentrate. Add the mint, reserving the top leaves for decoration. Cook gently, covered, for about 15 minutes until apples become a pulp, stirring occasionally. Discard the mint, then beat the pulp hard with a wooden spoon until it becomes smooth. This may be done alternatively using an electric blender, or by passing through a sieve. Leave the mixture to cool. Beat the egg whites until stiff, then fold into the apple mixture. Spoon into individual glasses and decorate with the reserved mint leaves. Serve chilled.

Suitable for Vegetarians   Serves 4

Yogurt Snow (cream substitute)

200g (8oz) Greek sheeps milk yogurt

2 tablespoons apple concentrate

2 egg whites

Method

Separate eggs carefully making sure none of the yolk gets into the whites. Place the two egg whites in a bowl and whisk until they form peaks and are stiff. Whisk in the apple concentrate until the mixture is very thick. Fold in the yogurt carefully and serve immediately instead of cream.

Suitable for Vegetarians   Makes about 450ml (¾pt)

Citrus Sorbet

2 grapefruit (preferably pink)

2 heaped teaspoons agar agar or gelatin, (dissolved in 2
   tablespoons water)

600ml (1pt) fresh grapefruit juice

150g (5.2oz) goats or sheeps yogurt

2 egg whites, stiffly beaten

8 mint or raspberry leaves to decorate

Method

Wash the grapefruits well and finely grate the rind from both into a large
bowl and add just enough boiling water to cover. Leave to soak for 5
minutes and then drain. Cut the grapefruits in half and squeeze thoroughly so that the flesh comes out with juice. Add to the soaked rind,
together with the dissolved gelatine or agar or agar, grapefruit juice and
yogurt. Stir well and then transfer to a rigid freezer proof container,
cover with cling film and freeze for about 1 hour, or until just beginning
to freeze round the edges. Whisk, then fold in the egg whites. Partly
freeze and whisk twice more. Cover, seal and freeze until firm. Transfer
to the refrigerator 10 minutes before serving to soften. Scoop into
chilled glasses and decorate with the leaves to serve.

Note.

This recipe can be used with any citrus fruits with good results. Choose
from orange, lemon, tangerine, satsuma or lime.

Suitable for Vegetarians   Serves 8

Chocolate Sponge and Sauce

110g (4oz) dairy free margarine

1 tablespoon apple concentrate

2 eggs beaten

110g (4oz) brown rice flour

2 level teaspoons raw cocoa powder

1½ level teaspoons baking powder

2 tablespoons water

Method

Put the margarine and apple concentrate in a large bowl and mix together until well blended. Add the beaten eggs a little at a time. Sieve together the flour, baking powder and cocoa powder. Beat into the creamed mixture, together with the water. Grease a pudding basin and put mixture into it. Bake it at 180°C (350°F) Gas Mark 4 for 45 - 55 mins. Serve with Chocolate Sauce.

Suitable for Vegetarians   Serves 4

Chocolate Sauce

30g (1oz) dairy free margarine

15g (½oz) cornflour

250ml (½pt) goats, sheeps or soya milk

2 teaspoons cocoa powder

Method

Melt the margarine in a saucepan, remove from the heat and blend in the cornflour. Stir in the milk and cocoa powder, bring to the boil and simmer for two minutes while stirring. Pour over the chocolate pudding and serve.

This recipe works equally well with carob powder if preferred.

Granny's Home Made Blueberry Pie pictured page 134

½k (1lb) blueberries

1 tablespoon apple concentrate

2 tablespoons water

dessert pastry (made up to recipe on page 142)

Method

Place the blueberries in a saucepan together with the water and apple concentrate, cook gently for 10 to 15 minutes or until the fruit is soft and tender. Strain the fruit, reserving the juice. Divide the pastry into two equal parts and roll out one part to line a pie dish. Put a pie funnel or upturned egg cup in the centre and pour the fruit around it on top of the pastry. Roll out second piece of pastry and roll it around the rolling pin. Gently roll it into place on top of the pie. Seal the edges with a fluted pattern or mark gently all round with a fork. Holding the pie in one hand, cut the excess pastry away. If desired form the leftover pastry pieces into leaves and berries to decorate the top. Cut a slit in the centre to allow the steam to escape and bake in a medium oven 190°C (375°F) Gas Mark 5 for 15 to 20 minutes. Serve hot with the reserved juice as a sauce or mix the juice with goats or sheeps yogurt to use as an interesting substitute for cream. Or try Yogurt Ice Cream (page 118)

Note.

This recipe works just as well with blackberries or apples as a filling.

Suitable for Vegetarians

SNACKS

Corn and Potato Stick Snack pictured page 75

2 packets potato sticks (unflavoured, ingredients, potato and salt only)

200g (8oz) popping corn kernels

2 tablespoons vegetable oil   ½ teaspoon sea salt

1oz sunflower seeds   1oz pumpkin seed

Method

Heat the oil in a large pan over a high heat. When oil is really hot add the popcorn kernels. Cover the pan quickly; shake continuously over the heat until the popping stops. Be sure to use a large enough pan to accommodate the volume as the popcorn expands. Combine with potato sticks, sunflower seeds, pumpkin seeds and salt. Toss all ingredients well together and eat now, or store in an airtight container.

Suitable for Vegetarians

Garlic Flavoured Popcorn

200g (8oz) popping corn kernels   ¼ - ½ teaspoon sea salt

2 tablespoons vegetable oil

¼ - ½ teaspoon garlic powder (according to taste)

Method

Heat the oil in a large saucepan over high heat. When the oil is really hot add the popcorn kernels. Cover the pan; shaking continuously over the heat until the popping stops. Be sure to use a large enough pan to allow for the volume as the popcorn expands. Combine the garlic powder and sea salt in a small bowl and sprinkle it over the popcorn. Toss to ensure the popcorn is evenly coated and eat hot or cold. Can be stored in an airtight container.

Note.

The traditional way to eat popped corn is with only salt to flavour it. If you prefer it that way, just omit the garlic powder.

Do not over indulge in these snacks as they are high in carbohydrates.

Suitable for Vegetarians

Garlic and Onion Crisps

1 large potato, sliced very thinly

¼ -½ teaspoon garlic salt

¼ -½ teaspoonful onion salt

1 litre (1.75pts) cooking oil of choice

Method

Heat the oil in a deep fry pan until it is smoking hot. Drop the potato slices into the hot oil individually, separating them with a utensil until they turn golden and float. Remove them and place in a dish lined with kitchen paper to drain. Keep repeating this process, frying the potato slices in batches of a few at a time (depending on the size of your pan) usually 6 - 10 slices. When all the potato slices have been cooked and drained, place them all into a bowl. Combine the onion and garlic salt and mix well. Sprinkle over the crisps, tossing gently to ensure they are evenly coated. Eat hot or cold. Can be stored in an airtight container, when cold.

Notes.

In most stores it is now possible to buy plain crisps, the ingredients of which are simply potatoes, salt and vegetable oil. You may find these adequate to your needs and certainly more convenient if you have a busy life style, however this simple technique allows you to have natural flavouring that is acceptable to the diet plan, avoiding artificial additives. Some prefer to leave the skins on the potato crisps. It certainly adds extra flavour. It is possible to purchase special slicers to help you get the very thin slices required to make super crispy crisps. The thinner the slices, the better the finished snack.

Do not overindulge in this snack as it is carbohydrate.

Suitable for Vegetarians

Jamaican Cornmeal Pone

250g (8oz) pumpkin, peeled

250g (8oz) dessicated coconut

1 teaspoon ground pimentos

½ teaspoon sea salt

125g (4oz) coarse cornmeal

1 tablespoon melted dairy free margarine

a little goats, sheeps or soya milk

Method

Grate the raw pumpkin and mix with the coconut, ground pimentos and cornmeal, stir in the melted margarine and a little of the milk to make a fairly stiff batter. Beat for a minute or two. Pour into a shallow, greased baking tin and bake in the oven at 180°C (350°F) Gas Mark 4 for about 30 minutes until cooked and firm to touch. Cut into neat pieces about 4cm (1½inch) x 6.5cm (2½inch) and serve hot or cold.

Note.

Very good served hot with concentrated, sugar free soya milk as a cream substitute, for a pudding.

Suitable for Vegetarians

Oat Flapjacks

300g (10oz) rolled oats

125g (4oz) dairy free margarine

4 tablespoons concentrated apple juice

Method

Rub the margarine well into the rolled oats; add the apple juice and mix well. Place into a well greased 18cm (7inch) square baking tin. Cook at 180°C (350°F) Gas Mark 4 for 20 to 30 minutes. Allow to cool for 10 minutes then cut into desired size pieces. Store in an airtight container.

Suitable for Vegetarians

Savoury Corn Nibbles

350g (12oz) coarse corn meal

2 free range eggs

150ml (6fl oz) water (approximately)

4 teaspoons vegetable, bouillon or yeast free stock powder

Method

Mix the corn meal, eggs and a little water in a bowl. Beat together to form a stiff batter, adding more water as necessary. Add the bouillon and beat again until thoroughly mixed in. Grease a flat baking sheet well and spread the mixture thinly over the bottom of the sheet. Bake in the middle of the oven at 180°C (350°F) Gas Mark 4 for 30 minutes or until firm on top and leaving the sides of the tin. Cool for a few minutes and then cut into 5cm (2inch) squares. Remove from the tin and eat as required. Good with hummus or other dip. Can be stored in an airtight container.

This recipe can be varied by using mixed spice, ginger or curry powder as alternative flavourings, using the same amount (4 teaspoons).

Do not over indulge. This snack is high in carbohydrate.

Suitable for Vegetarians

Oat Muffins

4 cups oat flour (made easily by grinding porridge oats in a liquidiser)

2 cups soya flour

4 large eggs made up to 4 cups liquid with equal parts of sheeps milk and water

pinch sea salt

Method

Put both flours and the salt in a bowl and mix together. Make a well in the centre and pour in the beaten eggs with the milk and water added. Beat to a batter by hand or with a food mixer. Grease 12 patty tins (usually come in trays of four). Cook in a hot oven at 200°C (400°F) Gas Mark 6 for about 30 minutes until well risen and firm to touch. Place on a wire rack to cool, then wrap in batches and deep freeze until required.

WAFFLES

Waffles are traditionally thought of as being stuffed full of sweet things for a dessert, American snack or breakfast, but they are very flexible and can be made with a great variety of flours, making them an ideal inclusion in a restricted diet. Here is a basic recipe. You will find a list of flours that work in it below.

170g (6oz) flour, meal or flakes

1 tablespoon oil of choice

1 egg

pinch of sea salt

2 level teaspoons baking powder, (wheat free if necessary)

2 teaspoons apple concentrate, (after the first month only)

125-250ml (5-10fl.oz) goats, sheeps or soya milk

Method

Mix all the ingredients except the milk together in a bowl, add 125ml (5fl.oz) milk and beat well, adding more as necessary until the batter is thick and smooth. (The amount of milk will vary with the type of flour being used). Leave to stand while the waffle iron is heating up. Adjust the consistency with more milk if necessary, as the mixture will thicken while standing. Brush the waffle iron with oil thoroughly. Use approximately 1½ tablespoons of batter for each waffle. Cook for 3-4 minutes approximately. Serve hot for breakfast instead of toast, or for a base with snacks. If cooked in batches, they freeze well.

Flours, meals and flakes that will make good waffles.

banana flour	chick pea flour
barley flour	millet flour or flakes
brown rice flour	oatmeal and porridge oats
buckwheat flakes	rye flour
chestnut flour	sorgum meal

Suitable for vegetarians

DIPS
Guacamole Dip

1 large ripe avocado, peeled and stoned
1 clove garlic
1 small red onion, chopped
juice of ½ lemon
½ teaspoon sea salt
¼ teaspoon chilli powder
1 tomato, skinned

Method
Place all the ingredients together in a blender or food processor until smooth. Serve with crudités or yeast free crackers. Makes about 300ml (11fl. oz).

Note.
This is a Mexican recipe and if you like chilli, it will delight your palette when teamed with Mexican Tortillas (see page 136 breads section)

Suitable for vegetarians

GRAVY

250ml (½ pt) stock, or water

15g (½ oz) cornflour

1 teaspoon Swiss vegetable bouillon (yeast free) or stock cube

Method

Pour off most of the fat from the roasting tin and blend in the cornflour. Stir in the stock or water with the bouillon; bring them to the boil, stirring continuously. Boil for 1 minute, then season to taste.

Note.

To give your gravy the nice brown colour you are used to, try slicing some onions and frying them until they are really brown, (just before they burn,) then add your water or stock and thicken. The caramelised onion will give it both colour and added flavour.

BREADS

Since ordinary bread is out of the question because of its yeast content, this means you must either find a baker willing to bake small batches for you to freeze or manage on yeast free crispbreads, or make your own. If you opt for making your own, at least you will know exactly what your daily bread contains. Some are frightened by the thought, but making your own bread substitutes is not half as difficult as you think. When making yeast free bread, it is not necessary to wait around for the bread to 'prove' so the whole procedure takes only a fraction of the time involved in making ordinary bread. Have a go - you will enjoy the results.

Pitta bread pictured page 44

250g (8oz) flour (½ wholemeal, ½ unbleached self raising)

pinch of sea salt

5fl. oz (¼pt) warm water, (approx)

1 teaspoon baking powder

½ teaspoon apple concentrate, (after 1st month only)

Method

Mix the flour, salt and baking powder in a bowl. In another bowl mix the water and apple concentrate. Pour the water mixture into the flour and mix to a dough. Stand aside, covered with a cloth for 10 minutes. Divide into 4 pieces and knead or roll between palms into an oval 'sausage'. Roll out into a flat oval. Place into a lightly greased frying pan or onto a griddle and cook on both sides until air bubbles appear and bread is slightly browned.

Serves 4

Irish Soda Bread pictured page 133

500g (1lb) flour (½ wholemeal, ½ unbleached self raising)

1½ teaspoons baking powder   2 heaped tablespoons sheeps yogurt

½ teaspoon sea salt   approx ½pt soya, sheeps or goats milk

Method

Preheat oven to 200°C (400°F) Gas Mark 6. Combine flours, baking powder and salt. Mix well. Place milk and yogurt together in a jug and mix. Stir milk mixture into the flour mixture until a soft dough is achieved. Knead into a round on a floured surface. Place on baking sheet and cut a bold cross on top. Bake in oven for 25-30 minutes until hollow sounding when tapped.

Seeded Sandwich Bread Recipe page 135

Irish Soda Bread Recipe page 132

Granny's Home-made Blueberry Pie Recipe page 124

Seeded Sandwich Bread pictured page 133

350g (12oz) white, unbleached self raising flour

100g (4oz) wholemeal flour

3 teaspoons baking powder

1 tablespoon (heaped) mixed sunflower and pumpkin seeds, flaked almonds etc

225g (8oz) goats or sheeps milk yogurt

100ml (4fl.oz) goats or sheeps milk

1 teaspoon sea salt

Method

Mix the flours, baking powder, salt and seeds in a mixing bowl. Place the milk and yogurt together in a jug and mix until smooth. Make a well in the centre of the dry ingredients and pour in the milk mixture. Mix to a sticky dough. Flour hands and turn onto a floured board. Shape to fit into a bread tin. Cook for 1 hour or until the loaf sounds hollow when tapped in a preheated oven 200°C (400°F) Gas Mark 6.

When cold, this bread slices well for sandwiches. The recipe will also make a batch of tasty rolls. Freezes well.

To make garlic bread

Take as many slices as you need from a yeast free loaf (see bread section), and toast lightly on one side. Remove from grill and spread with 'garlic butter' on the untoasted side, replace under the grill until 'butter' is melted and the bread has become brown round the edges.

To make garlic butter

Place 50g (2oz) dairy free margarine in a small bowl. Crush 2 cloves garlic into it and mix together with a fork until the garlic is distributed evenly through the margarine. This can all be used immediately or sealed in an airtight container and stored in the fridge.

Pizza Base

250g (8oz) self raising flour

300ml (5fl.oz) soya, goats or sheeps milk

pinch of sea salt

Method

Mix all the ingredients together to form a dough. Knead until smooth. Shape into circle/s depending on the size of the pizza required. Add topping and bake for 15 to 20 minutes at 190°C (375°F) Gas Mark 5.

For topping see Pizza Topping pages 105 & 109

Mexican Tortillas

125g (4oz) maizemeal

125g (4oz) rye flour

5 tablespoons corn oil

225ml (8fl. oz) water (approx)

½ teaspoon salt

Method

Mix the flours together in a bowl and stir in the oil. Add the water gradually until it forms a soft slightly sticky dough. Knead well. Cover and leave in the bowl for about ½ hour. Divide into 5cm (2inch) cubes.Roll in palms into a ball and then roll out on a floured surface into 12cm (5inch) diameter circles. Cook the tortillas in an ungreased frying pan or a griddle over a high heat until bubbles appear; then turn over and cook the other side. Keep warm until the whole batch is completed. Serve as an accompaniment for soups or dips.

Note.

These are especially good when served with Guacamole Dip as a simple snack or as a starter to a main meal, since both are of Mexican origin and the flavours compliment each other.

Try them also with:

Mexican Stuffed Tomatoes (see page 86)

Guacamole Dip (see page 130)

Sorghum Bread

110g (4oz) sieved sorghum meal

2 tablespoons oil of choice (olive oil adds subtle flavour)

1 medium sized carrot, grated

2 eggs   1 teaspoon sea salt

200ml (8fl. oz) boiling water   2 tablespoons cold water

Method

Combine the flour, carrot, salt and oil in a bowl. Mix well. Stir in the boiling water. Separate the eggs, beat the yolks well and add 2 tablespoons of cold water and continue beating. Add the eggs to flour mixture. Fold in stiffly beaten egg whites. Shape the dough and place on an oiled baking tray. Bake at 180°C (350°F) Gas Mark 4 for about 40 minutes.

This recipe works equally well with millet.

Mixed Flour Bread

300g (10oz) brown rice flour

150g (5oz) gram flour

150g (5oz) corn flour

1½ teaspoons sea salt

2 teaspoons bicarbonate of soda

300ml (½pt) soya milk

2 tablespoons sunflower oil

5 tablespoons (4fl.oz) cold water

Method

Mix all the dry ingredients together and sieve into a mixing bowl. Make a well in the middle. Mix all other ingredients (milk, oil and water) together in a jug and pour into the well. Gradually work into a smooth dough. Divide into 2 loaf tins or form into 8 rolls. Cook for 1 hour or until loaf sounds hollow when tapped, in a preheated oven 200°C (400°F) Gas Mark 6. Can be eaten fresh, hot or cold, or wrapped and frozen. Makes good slices for toasting or for garlic bread.

CAKES

Coconut rice fingers

170g (6oz) brown rice flour

15g (½oz) sesame seeds

45g (1½oz) dessicated coconut (preservative free)

4 level teaspoons baking powder

pinch of salt

3 tablespoons oil of choice

250ml (9fl. oz) goats, sheeps or soya milk

1 free range egg

Method

Place all ingredients together in a large bowl; whisk well. Oil a flat baking sheet and pour the mixture into it. Bake in the oven at 220°C (425°F) Gas Mark 7 for 15-20 minutes. Leave in the tin until cool, then cut into 3cm (1¼inch) x 6cm (2½inch) fingers. Store in an airtight container.

Welsh cakes

450g (1lb) unbleached self raising flour

225g (8oz) dairy free margarine

100g (4oz) fresh ginger (chopped finely)

2 free range eggs

a little goats, sheeps or soya milk for mixing if necessary

Method

Sieve the flour and salt together into a mixing bowl. Rub in the margarine until the mixture resembles fine bread crumbs. Add the ginger and then the eggs. Mix to a stiff dough onto a floured board and roll out to a ½cm (¼inch) thickness. Cut with a 5cm (2inch) fluted pastry cutter or round shape cutter. Cook on a preheated lightly greased griddle, over medium heat until golden brown, turn and repeat until both sides are done.

Spicy Come Again Cake

250g (8oz) brown rice flour   125ml (4fl. oz) oil

2 teaspoons baking powder   2 teaspoons vanilla essence

1 tablespoon mixed spice   2 tablespoons apple concentrate

1 free range egg

Method

Place all the ingredients, except the eggs and apple concentrate into a bowl and mix together. Beat the eggs and add the apple concentrate. Add to the mixture. Place the mixture in a greased 18cm (7inch) cake tin, preferably with a removable bottom and cook in a preheated oven at 180°C (350°F) Gas Mark 4 for 1 hour or until risen, firm to the touch and golden brown.

Sponge Cakes

170g (6oz) brown rice flour

1½ level teaspoons baking powder

110g (4oz) dairy free margarine

2 tablespoons apple concentrate

2 eggs

paper cake cases

Method

Cream the margarine and the apple concentrate together in a mixing bowl until blended well. Crack the eggs into a bowl and whisk well, then add them to the margarine mixture a little at a time beating constantly. Fold in the flour and baking powder (after sieving together). Spoon into paper cases and bake at 200°C (400°F) Gas Mark 6 for 15 to 20 minutes

Note.

This mixture can be put on top of stewed fruit in season in an oven proof dish and baked as a delicious desert. Top with Yogurt Snow (see page121).

BISCUITS

Yearnshire Cookies

2 tablespoons porridge oats

2 tablespoons dessicated coconut (preservative free)

1 large carrot, puréed in a mixer or blender

75g (3oz) rice flour

35g (1½oz) dairy free margarine

little soya milk to mix

Method

Rub margarine into the flour then add all the other dry ingredients. Add the carrot purée and enough soya milk to bond the mixture together. Grease a baking tray and press the mixture into it with the back of a spoon. Bake for approximately 10 minutes in an oven at 180°C (350°F) Gas Mark 4. Allow to cool and cut into fingers.

Aunties Oaties

450g (1lb) organic oats

100g (4oz) dairy free margarine

pinch of sea salt

4 tablespoons apple concentrate

boiling water

Method

Place the oats and salt into a large mixing bowl and rub in the margarine until the oats begin to clog together. Add the apple concentrate and mix well. Now add enough boiling water to bind the mixture into a dough, taking care not to add too much water or the mixture will get too sticky to roll out. Either spread the mixture into the bottom of a baking tray and press down flat, or roll out and cut into biscuit shapes, and place on a baking tray. If mixture is too sticky to roll, flour the surface with fine oatmeal before rolling out.

Place in a preheated oven for 30 minutes at 180°C (350°F) Gas Mark 4. If the flat version has been made, allow to cool before cutting into 5 x 8cm (2 x 3inch) pieces.

Ginger Biscuits pictured page 75

225g (8oz) self raising flour   pinch of salt

150g (5oz) dairy free margarine   1 tablespoon apple concentrate

1 egg, beaten

2 heaped teaspoons ground ginger (or to taste)

Method

Sift the flour and salt into a mixing bowl and rub in the margarine. Add the ginger, egg and the apple concentrate. Mix to a stiff dough. Turn out onto a floured board and knead until smooth. Form into a ball, wrap in foil or place in a polythene bag and chill in the refrigerator for about 30 minutes. Roll the dough thinly on a floured board and then cut into rounds with a pastry cutter (approximately 5cm (2inch) in diameter) with a fluted edge. Place on a greased baking tray leaving room between them for spreading during cooking. Prick them all over with a fork and bake in a moderate oven 180°C (350°F) Gas Mark 4 for 10 to 15 minutes or until golden brown. Leave them to cool for a few minutes and then transfer to a wire rack to cool completely.

Note.

1 - 2 tablespoons of cocoa powder can be added instead of ginger, if preferred.

PASTRY
Savoury Suet Pastry

125g (4oz) brown rice flour

125g (4oz) gram flour

125g (4oz) corn flour

cold water to mix

pinch of sea salt

125g (4oz) vegetable suet (available health food stores)

Method

Place all the flours together in a bowl, and mix. Add salt and mix again. Add the water a little at a time until the right consistency is formed. Turn onto a floured board and roll out to the desired shape. Cooking time 20 minutes at 180°C (350°F) Gas Mark 4.

Dessert Pastry

225g (8oz) plain white unbleached flour

100g (4oz) dairy free margarine

1 tablespoon apple concentrate (available health stores)

1 tablespoon water

Method

Place the flour into a mixing bowl and rub in the margarine until the mix resembles bread crumbs. Add the apple concentrate and mix thoroughly with a fork. Add enough of the water to bind the pastry together to a suitable consistency for rolling. Shape as required and bake in a medium oven at 180°C (350°F) Gas Mark 4 for about 20 minutes

Dumplings

200g (6oz) unbleached self raising flour

50g (2oz) wholemeal flour

125g (4oz) vegetable suet

pinch sea salt

water to mix (approximately 75 - 100ml)

2 teaspoons finely chopped sage (optional)

Method

Mix the flours together with the salt and suet. Add the sage. Make a well in the centre and pour in the water, mixing to a sticky dough. Divide mixture into 6 pieces and roll in floured hands, to form balls. Float on top of stews for the last 20 - 30 minutes of cooking time. Can also be used as a topping for casseroles. Simply remove the lid 30 minutes before the end of cooking time in the oven and float the dumplings on the top. They will form a lovely crispy topping on one side and the traditional dumpling consistency on the other.

Suitable for vegetarians

DRESSINGS

Mustard Dressing

2 tablespoons lemon juice

1 teaspoon dry mustard

1 tablespoons olive oil

1 tablespoon chopped fresh mint

Method

Put dressing ingredients all together in a screw topped jar and shake well. Pour over salad, toss and serve.

Greek Island Dressing

100ml (4fl. oz) olive oil

1 clove garlic, crushed

sea salt and pepper

1 tablespoon finely chopped mint and oregano

juice of 1 lemon

1 tablespoon finely chopped chives

Method

Place all the ingredients together in a screw topped jar and shake together well. Makes 150ml (5fl. oz)

Note.

This dressing will separate if left to stand. Just shake again before serving.

Yogurt Salad Dressing

150ml (5fl oz) goats or sheeps yogurt

juice of 1 lemon

sea salt and pepper

2 tablespoon chopped chives

1 clove garlic, crushed

Method

Mix all the ingredients together and chill before serving. Makes 150ml (5fl. oz)

Green Yogurt Dressing

150ml (5fl.oz) goats or sheeps yogurt

juice of ½ small lemon

sea salt and pepper

2 tablespoons mayonnaise (see page 146)

4 tablespoons chopped fresh herbs (parsley, chives, tarragon, mint, basil)

Method

Place all the ingredients together in a bowl and mix well.

French Dressing

2 tablespoons olive oil

2 tablespoons fresh lemon juice

a pinch of mixed dried herbs (optional)

pinch sea salt

¼ - ½ teaspoon cumin

Method

Place all the ingredients in a screw topped jar and shake together until well mixed. Pour over salad and toss. Serve.

Note.

Will keep for up to three days in a refrigerator, covered. Shake before serving.

Garlic Dressing

Just use the basic french dressing recipe and add 2 cloves of crushed garlic to the list of ingredients.

Mayonnaise

1 free range egg

2 tablespoons fresh lemon juice

¼ to ½ teaspoon sea salt (optional)

1 teaspoon dry mustard (optional)

225ml (8fl.oz) 1 cup olive oil (other may be used if desired)

Method

Break the egg into a bowl or blender and beat well. If using a blender use slow speed. Add lemon juice, (mustard and salt if desired). Continue blending, adding the oil really slowly by dribbling the oil down the back of a fork, beating continuously until the mayonnaise is thick and all the oil has been used. To change the flavour you can use, not only the mustard suggested above, but a clove of crushed garlic or a ½ teaspoon of curry powder.

Note.

1) Don't worry about the stories you have heard, mayonnaise is very easy to make. It will only curdle if you put too much oil in at a time.

2) This recipe will keep in a screw topped jar in the refrigerator for 2 to 3 days, but don't risk it for longer.

3) This mayonnaise can be used as a vegetable dip with crudités or as a sea food sauce with a little tomato purée added to give it colour.

NUTS

Nuts have been deliberately excluded from the recipes and snack suggestions because so many Candida (and allergy) sufferers, experience serious problems with them. This does not mean that EVERYONE must exclude them, but all should be tested for tolerance before including them. There are some nuts however that MUST BE AVOIDED, they are:- PEANUTS, PISTACHIOS AND BRAZILS because they are known to produce a high ratio of mould. If your allergy tests prove negative to all the others, then you may include them in your diet.

DRINKS

Any fruit teas can now be included in your regime.

Such as:- apple, rosehip, strawberry, orange, lemon, lime etc... Also available to you now are fruit juices, but they must be fresh squeezed and do not overindulge, as the fructose content is high. If your symptoms start to return when you include these on a regular basis, drop them again and wait for a while longer before reintroducing them. A good compromise would be to drink them at first, watered down with carbonated or plain spring water in a half and half mix.

You may also include alcohol in small quantities now, but only 2 spirits are acceptable, they are vodka and gin. When socialising ask for:-

1) A Pink Gin
This is a dash of angostura aromatic bitters swirled around a gin glass and the excess discarded, the measure of gin is then added to the glass giving it a pink appearance. It can be made into a longer drink by adding Perrier water, in a tall glass.

2) Bloody Mary
This is a measure of vodka mixed together with a pure tomato juice.

You will no doubt find a number of ways to enjoy these two spirits. For instance:- gin and orange and vodka and lime are well known combinations but it may be difficult to find pure fruit mixers without additives when drinking in bars and clubs.

Some bars are pleased to offer Perrier natural, with lemon or lime, and Piermont sparkling spring water with apple or blackberry juice as another option. Aqua Libra and Sorrel are two bottled water and fruit juice drinks that can be drunk as they are, or used as mixers. Both are available in most health food shops and supermarkets. Do watch mixer drinks for additives and artificial colourings.

Of course the inclusion of alcohol into your regime is a personal decision but if too much is consumed, it could affect the speed of your recovery. **Caution is therefore strongly urged.**

STAGE 3

At the end of six months.

By the time you reach this stage you should be feeling really well again. If not, then you must continue with Stage 2 until all your Candida symptoms have disappeared. The length of time will depend on how ill you were when you began. Six months has been set because it is an AVERAGE period in which MOST people return to optimum health, but it is by no means a fixed time for everyone and must be viewed with flexibility.

It would be sensible to consult a practitioner again to make absolutely sure that your Candida has returned to a normal level, (Vega and A.K. tests, in the hands of capable practitioners can be reliable), before embarking on this last stage. They will also advise you on how to begin reducing your supplements in a proper manner.* If the Candida overgrowth has been curbed, then you will no longer need an antifungal agent, but it may be necessary to continue taking lowered dosages of the vitamin, mineral and probiotic supplements for a while longer to ensure your immune system is fully strengthened against further attacks. This is also advisable if, although having successfully brought the Candida under control, you discover you still have some food allergies lingering.

If you have been scrupulous about keeping the rules of the diet, you will by now have formed improved eating habits and persuaded your taste buds against an unhealthy diet. It would be extremely unwise to return to the old way of eating, as it was probably a contributing factor in your original illness.

Remember, as you reintroduce foods into your diet, these two simple slogans:-

Brown is best, refined should be declined.

If it doesn't go bad, it's not fit to be had. (It will be full of preservatives).

When you are sure all is well, you can begin to reintroduce yeast, sugars and cow's milk products, coffee and tea etc., but one at a time, over a period of weeks, just as you did in the second stage. In the first week you can start by having wholemeal bread with yeast (preservative free) but only on three days, leaving a day without in between. On the alternate days, you may add honey or fructose. When you are sure there are no adverse reactions, then you may introduce bovine products such as cows milk, cheese, butter and cream. It is not recommended you use cheeses such as Stilton, Gorgonzola or Roquefort at this stage. In fact some people decide never to resume eating mould carrying foods again as they fear they may always be susceptible.

To show you how to proceed, 4 weekly menu plan charts have been prepared using the recipes contained in this book. The charts are not necessarily intended to be followed exactly, but are meant as a guide for you. Vegetarians should adapt in a similar way. Each individual has distinctly personal likes and dislikes and will probably develop a way of eating to suit their lifestyle, including favourite dishes they have developed or discovered themselves, therefore there is another blank chart for planning convenience. If at any time during the next 4 weeks you experience a return of any previous symptoms, stop the re-introductory process, or at the very least the food causing the problem, wait a few weeks and then try again, meanwhile continuing with the supplement programme. Some people do not regain full immunity to everything for 2 - 3 years, so don't be too disappointed, or expect too much too soon.

Now you are ready to embark on a way of eating designed to keep you fit and healthy for the rest of your life.

*See page 164 'Food Supplements Necessary to Complete the Programme.'

WEEK 1   MEAT EATERS DIET PLAN

	BREAKFAST	LUNCH	DINNER
MONDAY	Breakfast in a Glass with **WHOLEMEAL TOAST (YEAST)**	Italian Minestrone Soup with yeast free rolls	Prawn (Shrimp) Apple and Celery Cocktail Beef with Orange and Veg. Apple and Pear Crumble
TUESDAY	Home made Baked Beans on Pitta Bread	Tabouleh Salad	Egg Mayonnaise Lamb Provencal Yogurt with **HONEY (SUGAR)**
WEDNESDAY	Herb Fish Cakes	Leek & Potato Soup **& BREAD (YEAST)**	Baba Ghanoush Columbian Turkey Citrus Sorbet
THURSDAY	Hearty Start Fruity Herb tea with **HONEY**	Cauliflower & Apple Crunch	Mexican Stuffed Tomatoes & Tortillas. Chilli Bean Casserole Granny's Home-made Blueberry Pie with Yogurt Snow
FRIDAY	Asparagus Omelette	French Onion Soup & Sandwich Bread	Falafel Mediterranean Fish Stew Fresh Fruit Salad topped with **HONEY (SUGAR)**
SATURDAY	Granola & sheeps milk yogurt	Jacket Potatoes with filling	Chilled Avocado Soup **BREAD ROLLS (YEAST)** Rabbit with Mustard Sauce Spicy Surprise
SUNDAY	Onion Hash Browners with egg & bacon	Caponata Style Fetuccine	Cretan Sheeps Feta Salad & Pitta Bread Guinea Fowl with Raspberries Chocolate Pudding & Sauce

WEEK 2   MEAT EATERS DIET PLAN

	BREAKFAST	LUNCH	DINNER
MONDAY	Breakfast in a Glass with **WHOLEMEAL TOAST (YEAST)**	Italian Minestrone Soup with yeast free rolls	Prawn (Shrimp) Apple&Celery Cocktail. Beef with Orange and Veg. Apple and Pear Crumble **FRUCTOSE** in crumble **(SUGAR)**
TUESDAY	Home made Baked Beans on **BREAD (YEAST)**	Tabouleh Salad	Egg Mayonnaise Lamb Provencal Yogurt with **HONEY (SUGAR)**
WEDNESDAY	Herb Fish Cakes Coated with **BREADCRUMBS (YEAST)**	Leek & Potato Soup & **BREAD (YEAST)**	Baba Ghanoush. Columbian Turkey. Citrus Sorbet **FRUCTOSE** to sweeten **(SUGAR)**
THURSDAY	Hearty Start	Cauliflower & Apple Crunch **BREAD (YEAST)**	Mexican Stuffed Tomatoes & Tortillas. Chilli Bean Casserole Granny's Home-made Blueberry Pie with Yogurt Snow
FRIDAY	Asparagus Omelette	French Onion Soup & Sandwich Bread	Falafel Mediterranean Fish Stew Fresh Fruit Salad topped with **HONEY (SUGAR)**
SATURDAY	Granola & sheeps milk yogurt **HONEY (SUGAR)**	Jacket Potatoes with filling	Chilled Avocado Soup **BREAD ROLLS (YEAST)** Rabbit with Mustard Sauce Spicy Surprise
SUNDAY	Onion Hash Browners with egg & bacon	Caponata Style Fetuccine **BREAD (YEAST)**	Cretan Sheeps Feta Salad & Pitta Bread. Guinea Fowl with Raspberries.Chocolate Pudding & Sauce. **FRUCTOSE (SUGAR)**

WEEK 3   MEAT EATERS DIET PLAN

	BREAKFAST	LUNCH	DINNER
MONDAY	Breakfast in a Glass with **WHOLEMEAL TOAST (YEAST) & BUTTER (COW'S MILK)**	Italian Minestrone Soup with **BREAD ROLLS (YEAST)**	Prawn (Shrimp) Apple & Celery Cocktail. Beef with Orange & Veg. Apple & Pear Crumble **FRESHCREAM (COW'S MILK) FRUCTOSE** in crumble
TUESDAY	Home made Baked Beans on **BREAD (YEAST)**	Tabouleh Sald	Egg Mayonnaise Lamb Provencal Turkey, Citrus Sorbet **YOGURT (COW'S MILK)** with **HONEY (SUGAR)**
WEDNESDAY	Herb Fish Cakes Coated with **BREADCRUMBS (YEAST)**	Leek & Potato Soup with Pitta Bread	Baba Ghanoush. Columbian Turkey. Citrus Sorbet **FRUCTOSE** to sweeten **(SUGAR)**
THURSDAY	Hearty Start	Cauliflower & Apple Crunch **BREAD (YEAST)**	Tortillas, Chilli Bean Casserole. Granny's Homemade Blueberry Pie with **FRESH CREAM (COW'S MILK)** Mexican Stuffed Tomatoes &
FRIDAY	Asparagus Omelette **BREAD (YEAST)**	French Onion Soup & Sandwich Bread	Falafel Mediterranean Fish Stew Fresh Fruit Salad topped with **HONEY (SUGAR)**
SATURDAY	Granola & sheeps milk yogurt **HONEY (SUGAR)**	Jacket Potatoes with filling **CHEESE (COW'S MILK)**	Chilled Avocado Soup **BREAD ROLLS (YEAST)** Rabbit with Mustard Sauce Spicy Surprise topped with **BUTTER (COW'S MILK)**
SUNDAY	Onion Hash Browners with egg & bacon	Caponata Style Fettuccine **BREAD (YEAST)**	Cretan Sheeps Feta Salad & Pitta Bread. Guinea Fowl with Raspberries, Chocolate Pudding & Sauce. **FRUCTOSE** to sweeten **(SUGAR)**

WEEK 4

MEAT EATERS DIET PLAN

	BREAKFAST	LUNCH	DINNER
MONDAY	Breakfast in a Glass with **WHOLEMEAL TOAST (YEAST) & BUTTER (COW'S MILK)**	Italian Minestrone Soup with **BREAD ROLLS (YEAST) TEA**	Prawn (Shrimp) Apple & Celery Cocktail. Beef with Orange & Veg. Apple & Pear Crumble **FRESHCREAM (COW'S MILK) FRUCTOSE** in crumble
TUESDAY	Sugar Free, Shop Bought Baked Beans on **BREAD (YEAST) COFFEE**	Tabouleh Salad **ADD OLIVES**	Egg Mayonnaise Lamb Provencal **YOGURT (COW'S MILK)** with **HONEY (SUGAR)**
WEDNESDAY	Herb Fish Cakes Coated with **BREADCRUMBS (YEAST)**	Leek & Potato Soup with Pitta Bread **TEA**	Baba Ghanoush. Columbian Turkey. Citrus Sorbet **FRUCTOSE** to sweeten (SUGAR)
THURSDAY	Hearty Start **COFFEE**	Cauliflower & Apple Crunch **BREAD (YEAST)**	Mexican Stuffed Tomatoes & Tortillas. Chilli Bean Casserole Granny's Homemade Blueberry Pie with **FRESH CREAM (COW'S MILK)**
FRIDAY	Asparagus Omelette **BREAD (YEAST)**	French Onion Soup & Sandwich Bread **TEA**	Falafel Mediterranean Fish Stew Fresh Fruit Salad topped with **HONEY (SUGAR) ADD GRAPES**
SATURDAY	Granola & sheeps milk yogurt **HONEY (SUGAR)**	Jacket Potatoes with filling **CHEESE (COW'S MILK)**	Chilled Avocado Soup **BREAD ROLLS (YEAST)** Rabbit with Mustard Sauce Spicy Surprise topped with **BUTTER (COW'S MILK)**
SUNDAY	Onion Hash Browners with egg & bacon **COFFEE**	Caponata Style Fetuccine **BREAD (YEAST)**	Cretan Sheeps Feta Salad & Pitta Bread **ADD OLIVES**. Guinea Fowl with Raspberries. Chocolate Pudding & Sauce. **FRUCTOSE** to sweeten (SUGAR)

MENU PLANNER

	BREAKFAST	LUNCH	DINNER
MONDAY			
TUESDAY			
WEDNESDAY			
THURSDAY			
FRIDAY			
SATURDAY			
SUNDAY			

EATING OUT

Many Candida sufferers dismiss the idea of eating out whilst they are following their diet. They think it will be just too complicated, but the problems can be easily overcome with a little forward planning. A positive approach will make a meal away from home a success.

Make for yourself two lists, the first of things you can eat, and the other, of foods you must avoid, then make sure you always keep copies with you. If you know where you will be eating then simply call in, phone or write a few days prior to your arrival. Explain your problem to the chef and give him / her copies of your lists. All they need is a little advanced warning and time to prepare and plan a wonderful meal for you. Friends too will be happy to help if you let them know of your problem and provide alternative suggestions.

However it may not always be possible to know in advance where you will be eating so you will need to learn how to examine the menu in any restaurant you visit, with care. Also enlist the help of the waiter or waitress to find out what each dish contains. Again your lists will be invaluable to you in making a selection. Whilst there will probably be starters and main courses that are easily adapted to your needs by omitting sauces and dressings, you may find that you will have to avoid the sweet course entirely, or (after the first month) opt for a piece of fresh fruit.

Quick snacks and fast foods can also be useful to you. Things such as jacket potatoes, fish, chips, kebabs and salads are not difficult to find, but do remember to leave out the sauces and dressings.

Many people prefer to take their own snacks out with them. They choose to pack lunches that include things like cartons of live yogurt, pre-cooked rice with diced raw vegetables and seeds added, crisps, sandwiches made from yeast free bread or home made soups and stews in wide necked Thermos flasks. (see page 161)

Whichever way you choose to eat outside of your own home, remember that planning ahead will make it easier to maintain your diet. Don't be shy or afraid to ask for what you need, generally people will be very happy to help you when you explain that your health depends on it. **Communication is the key to success.**

MAINTAINING THE DIET ON HOLIDAY

Holidays are times for relaxation but not for relaxing the rules of your diet. Advance planning as always is the key to holiday eating success.

Choose your destination carefully bearing in mind that of necessity, you will encounter certain restrictions. Once you have decided where to go you can then begin planning how to cope. If your holiday is to be spent in a hotel or a guest house then simply send your 'Eating Out' lists ahead before you book to make sure that your diet will not present problems for the proprietors. If it does, book elsewhere.

Foreign holidays need extra attention. You can order 'in flight meals' when booking and they can be made up to your individual requirements. It would be wise to pack something to carry with you in case of delays. You will find it advantageous to acquire a dual lingual dictionary and take time to translate your food lists into the language of the country you wish to visit. You will then be equipped to read menus and recognise the appropriate foods to fit in with your dietary needs. Prior enquiry about the cuisine of the country and the availability of your specialised foods would be sensible. If you discover that certain items may be difficult to find or totally unobtainable, then you must be prepared to take those items with you. For instance, you may find dairy free margarine, goats, sheeps, or soya milk and cheese will be unobtainable. Or that yeast free stock cubes, bouillon and crackers just don't exist there. If you plan to self cater then, pack some of your favourite herbs and spices and a few essential cooking implements such as your own sharp knife, a grater and a hand whisk. With these few items you can turn virtually anything into a meal.

Don't forget pitta bread can be made over a single gas or electric ring, flour of some kind and water is available everywhere.

When shopping at your holiday location, rise early and follow the local housewives to the market, they will lead you to the best produce available, and if you speak their language or they speak yours, they will gladly advise you where to find the 'best buys'.

Sampling the cuisine of another country can add 'flavour' to your holiday and often you can take home new ideas to expand your menu.

Helpful notes.
Powdered goats milk is available in Health Shops, it is light for aircraft baggage.
Sheeps cheese in wax travels well.

ENTERTAINING AT HOME

Most cookbooks worth their 'salt', have a section on planning a dinner party, but experience tells me that most people with a Candida problem do not feel remotely inclined to expend the effort required on throwing a 'soiree'. Unless it is absolutely essential for your job, or a social necessity (if such thing exists), then you shouldn't even think of it while you are ill. Concentrate all the energy you have on getting well.

Something that may be possible though is a quiet meal, shared with a kindly considerate friend (or couple), who are not too demanding and are prepared to leave early in order not to wear you out. Any of the recipes contained in this book will be suitable. Bearing in mind your energy is limited, it would be best to choose simple things to offer, such as:-

Cretan Feta Cheese Salad (no cooking and quick to prepare in advance).

A Roast of choice (throw it in the oven and go and lay down for a couple of hours).

You could choose an exotic meat such as venison, peacock or wild boar. You wouldn't even have to go out to shop for these, just phone the order through and they will be delivered to your door (see useful addresses page 170)

If your friends are vegetarian, then a Chilli or a Aduki Bean Casserole will need little time in preparation and simmer away merrily while you take your rest.

A 'bought-in' gateau takes care of a sweet course for your guests, and you can have a plain yogurt or a Beet Treat.

Good humour and pleasant conversation will make up for culinary deficiencies and the evening will be uplifting, not exhausting. So enjoy yourself...... but gently.

IDEAS FOR PRACTICAL PACKED LUNCHES

1) A variety of lightweight containers with lids (can be a special purchase or a collection of empty margarine or other cartons)
2) Small sharp knife (with sheath)
3) Bottle opener
4) Kitchen roll
5) Wide necked thermos flask
6) Kitchen foil
7) Tin opener
8) Non P.V.C. cling film
9) Knife, fork and spoon
10) Plastic or disposable plate(s)
11) Plastic cup
12) Soft, collapsible cold bag

First do a reconnaissance trip round your local food store and see what you can purchase ready prepared and wrapped. You should be able to find things like:-

Rice cakes

Oat cakes

Rye crispbreads

Matzos Crackers

Unflavoured crisps (read labels carefully)

Tortilla chips (read labels carefully)

Canned carbonated spring water

Bottled carbonated spring water

Plain spring water

After the first month:-

Aqua Libra, Perrier with lemon or lime or similar canned or bottled products (check labels carefully for additives)

Pilchards, mackerel, tuna, salmon canned in brine, spring water or oil

Specialist soups in cans

Live Greek sheeps or goats yogurt

Hummus

Goats and sheeps milk cheese

These foods will make for variety and convenience.

Practical Packed Lunches

Now add these home made items, some of which you can prepare in batches and keep ready wrapped in the refrigerator.

Tabouleh (bulgar wheat salad) see page 99

Rice Salad (see recipe page 162)

Couscous with chopped raw vegetables

Sprouted pulses (instructions page 73)

Mackerel in a tin

Hummus and crudités (see pages 42 & 74)

Cheeses (goats and sheeps)

Potato Salad (see recipe page 95)

Tuna in a tin

Hot soup or stew in Thermos

Pilchards in a tin

Cold roast chicken

Cold meat cuts

All salad ingredients

Sandwiches made with yeast free bread (see suggested fillings page 163)

Pitta bread

Soda bread

Mayonnaise (in a small screw topped container (see recipe page 146)

Fresh fruit (after first month)

To make an enviable meal, take cold meat of choice and place on a plastic or disposable plate; surround it with fresh salad ingredients e.g. lettuce, tomato, cucumber, onion, celery, raw carrot, cauliflower florets, radishes etc.. Take a long piece of cling film and wrap it around the entire plate. Place in your cold bag together with cutlery wrapped in serviettes or kitchen roll. Now add a small carton of potato salad to add at the time of eating. A carton of yogurt and (after 1st month) a piece of fresh fruit, plus a can or bottle of sparkling spring water and bread or crackers of your choice, and you have a really healthy meal that will not compromise your diet. You will soon think of lots of great meal ideas to take out with you.

160

Warming Winter Stew

Boil up the leftover chicken carcass to create a nutritious stock. Leave the stock to stand and strain off the layer of fat that forms. Pick all the small pieces of meat from the bones and leave in the stock. Now chop:-

1 onion

1 carrot

1 small turnip

1 small parsnip

a handful of sprouts

½ a small swede

1 potato

2 sticks celery

1 small orange or satsuma (segmented) after first month

sea salt and pepper

Method

Chop or dice all the vegetables as appropriate and place in a large saucepan. Add the chicken stock and any broth that has been saved from the cooking, salt and pepper to taste and bring to the boil. Simmer for 20 to 30 minutes or until all the vegetables are tender. Fill a wide necked Thermos flask to the top with the stew and seal tightly.

This recipe will work with any diced meat, fresh or leftovers, but if fresh see that the meat is thoroughly cooked through. It could be fried off before adding to the vegetables. If there is any left over in the pan, it can be transferred into a freezer proof container and frozen for future use.

* Vegetarians should use a vegetable stock for a base, the same selection of vegetables, but add the pulses of their choice.

Other vegetarian alternatives could be Curried Vegetables (from the recipe on page 70) or Chilli Beans (recipe page 114) Both can be carried in a flask to ensure they stay hot. Eat them with yeast free bread instead of the Couscous and rice.

Cold Rice Salad

225g (8oz) brown rice
1 teaspoon sea salt
750ml (1½ pts) water

Method

Place the water and salt in a large saucepan and bring to the boil. Add the rice and cook, covered until tender, about 20 to 30 minutes. Drain and place in freezer proof containers. When cold, seal in single portions and place in freezer.

When ready to pack lunch, remove the quantity of cooked rice needed (depending on size of appetite) from the container and allow to defrost. While defrosting take:-

2 spring onions

5cm (2inch) cucumber

1 small carrot

1 stick celery

½ green bell pepper

1 tomato

Chop or dice any or all of these vegetables and add to the rice. Seal in a container and it is ready to pack.

For variations of flavour try adding:-

1 teaspoon curry powder

French dressing (see page 145)

Meat eaters can mix in a drained can of tuna fish just before eating.

Vegetarians can make it up with added sprouted pulses.

SUGGESTIONS FOR
SANDWICH AND PITTA FILLINGS

Yeast free bread can be a bit dry if you are used to the store bought variety, so sandwich fillings need to be tasty and moist to make up for it. Here are a few delicious offerings:-

Tuna, drained and mashed with yogurt, lemon juice and cayenne pepper, and mixed with bean sprouts (O.K. for 1st month)

Kidney beans, cooked and mixed with tomato and green pepper (not for 1st month)

Lentils cooked to thick mush with apple, mixed spice and onion (not for 1st month)

Soft goats or sheeps cheese with chopped orange, watercress and pine kernels (leave out the orange for 1st month)

Hard boiled eggs, mashed, with home-made mayonnaise (O.K. for 1st month)

Tuna mashed in home-made mayonnaise with cucumber (O.K. for first month)

Potatoes, cooked, (leftovers) cubed, and mixed with chopped onions and chives bound together with mayonnaise. Add a little shredded lettuce. (not for 1st month)

Hummus with slices of cucumber (O.K. for 1st month)

Tzatsiki with tomato and sheeps cheddar (leave out tomato for first month)

Wensleydale sheeps cheese with sliced onion.

FOOD SUPPLEMENTS NECESSARY TO COMPLETE THE PROGRAMME

If you follow the foregoing diet plan carefully, you will have made an excellent start toward your aim of controlling your Candida overgrowth, **but diet alone will not achieve total success. YOU DO NEED SUPPLEMENTS,** to help your immune system to return to normality. Here is a brief summary of the supplements needed to complete the programme.

1) An antifungal agent
This should be a quality product, enterically coated to ensure it reaches the colon at full strength.

2) Probiotics
First, a really strong freeze dried strain of bifidus bifodum capable of yielding approx 30 billion organisms per teaspoon, followed later by an equally powerful strain of L'acidophilus.

3) Vitamins and Minerals
In order to supply what is needed to restore the immune system, these must be taken in megadoses.

	Required Daily
Vitamin A (Betacarotene)	10,500 iu
Vitamin E (d-Alpha Tocopherol)	195 iu
Vitamin C	3,000 mg
Vitamin B5 (Calcium Pantothenate)	600 mg
Magnesium Gluconate	300 mg
B1	104 mg
B3 (Nicotinamide)	104 mg
B2	60 mg
Vitamin B6	60 mg
Inositol	60 mg
Choline	60 mg
P.A.B.A.	60 mg
Zinc Gluconate	60 mg
Biotin	4.500 mcg
Folic Acid	60 mcg
Vitamin B12	60 mcg
Selenium (Seleniummethionine)	60 mcg

4) Garlic and Olive Oil

Even though they may be used daily in the diet it is important to ensure that enough of these two precious commodities are present in the system, so supplementation may be necessary.

A full explanation of the complete supplementary programme can be found in the book entitled "The Way Back, The A-Z of coping with M.E., Candida and Allergies." by the same author. (See page 176)

Where to obtain your supplements

Often difficulty is experienced locating the whole list of supplements in the precise quantities and strengths required.

The Earthdust Programme contains all these requirements and is available in monthly packs together with a booklet explaining how and when to take the supplements. All the vitamins and minerals are in a single capsule making them much easier to take and to carry about with you. Available by post from Earthdust Products, (see Useful Addresses page 170)

Earthdust Products are also distributors for the following vitamin and mineral companies:- Biocare, G & G, Natures Own, Quest, Cantassium, Malcolm Simmonds (herbalist), Natural Flow, Gerards etc....
They are happy to advise you on the product/s most suited to your individual needs.

Note.
All gelatin used for capsules is from safe sources.

COMPREHENSIVE LIST OF SYMPTOMS THAT MAY BE DUE TO CANDIDA ALBICANS

Below is a list of symptoms that can be expected to respond to the diet recommended in this book if they are caused by Candida.

GASTRO-INTESTINAL SYSTEM
adhesions
abdominal pain ✓
chronic heartburn ✓
excessive gas
rectal itching

gastritis
distention, bloating of abdomen
diarrhoea
haemorrhoids (piles)
mucous in stools ✓

EARS
recurring infections
deafness ✓
excessive wax ✓

pain
fluid in the ears
noises

EYES
spots on vision
tearing
blurred vision
double vision
night blindness ✓

burning
failing vision
erratic vision
chronic inflammation

MOUTH AND THROAT
sore and bleeding gums
sore and dry throat
blisters, ulcers ✓
bad breath ✓

coated tongue ✓
white patches
dry mouth
rash

SKIN
itching
psoriasis
acne
athlete's foot ✓
skin discolouration

rashes
dry scalp
dermatitis
fungal infections of skin
and nails ✓

MUSCULAR SKELETAL SYSTEM

muscle aches and pains
muscle paralysis
joint stiffness ✓
arthritis ✓

muscle weakness
joint pains
joint swelling
low back pain

NOSE AND SINUSES

nasal congestion and stuffiness
itching

post nasal drip ✓

LUNGS AND CHEST

persistent cough ✓
pain and tightness ✓
asthma

wheezing ✓
shortness of breath

URINARY SYSTEM

recurring kidney infections
recurring bladder infections
urethritis
burning on urination

cystitis
urinary infections
urgency to urinate ✓

EMOTIONAL/MENTAL NERVOUS SYSTEM

irritability
jittery behaviour ✓
sudden mood changes
depression
panic attacks
lethargy ✓
nervous exhaustion ✓
agitation

extreme mood changes ✓
inability to concentrate
poor memory ✓
acute anxiety
persistent headaches ✓
fatigue ✓
constant sleepiness ✓

CARDIOVASCULAR SYSTEM

mitral valve prolapse
tingling, numbness in extremities
palpitations
lack of libido ✓

poor circulation
cold hands and feet
sexual impotence

MISCELLANEOUS

increased body hair	loss of body hair
weight gain	hair breaking or falling
weight loss ✓	loss of balance ✓
poor coordination	dizziness
bad dreams	insomnia
loss of appetite	overreacting ✓
thymus imbalance	thyroid imbalances ✓

WOMEN

vaginal itching or burning	vaginal discharge ✓
endometriosis	menstrual cramps
failure to menstruate ✓	too frequent periods
premenstrual depression	scant menstrual flow
extremely heavy menstrual flow	premenstrual tension
soreness of breasts	non-cancerous lumps in breasts
thrush	

MEN

prostatitis	thrush under foreskin

ALLERGIC SYMPTOMS

hay fever	rhinitis ✓
hives	urticaria
food and chemical sensitivities ✓	asthma

Whilst no claims are made for an outright 'cure', clinical obser vation has noted that the following conditions have responded favourably to the Candida diet:-

allergies	Hodgkins disease
Crohn's disease	thyroid imbalances
systemic lupus erythematosus	scleroderma
sarcoidosis	chronic respiratory disease ✓
myasthenia gravis	autism
irritable bowl sydrome	anorexia nervosa
bulimia	multiple sclerosis ✱
drug addiction	inflammatory bowel disease
A.I.D.S	diabetes
cancer	epilepsy

List of symptoms found in children with Candida albicans

thrush	nappy rash
colic	irritability
recurring ear infections	hyperactivity
learning difficulties	short attention span ✗
nasal congestion ✗	chronic cough
wheezing	persistent headaches
digestive problems	constipation ✗
diarrhoea	gas and bloating
craving for sweets	mood swings
tonsillitis ✗	worm infestation

Children will also have a very 'pasty' grey complexion and often have dark rings under their eyes.

USEFUL ADDRESSES

Finding organic food can pose a problem in some areas, but here is a list of companies prepared to have items delivered to your door, either by post or courier. All you do is send an order by post, or telephone them.

The Real Meat Co. Ltd   (Contact Richard Guy)
Easthill Farm, Heyesbury, Wilts BA12 OHR
Tel: 01985 840562   Fax: 01985 841005

Heal Farm, Quality Traditional Meats   Contact Anne Peach
Kings Nympton, Umberleigh, Devon EX37 9TB
Tel: 0176 9574341   Fax: 0176 9572839
(Will make up speciality sausages leaving out rusk and preservatives)

Longwood Farm Organic Farmers and Butchers
Tuddenham, Bury - St - Edmunds, Suffolk, IP28 6TB
Contact Matthew or Louise Unwin   Tel/Fax 01638 717120

Barrow Boar
Fosters Farm, South Barrow, Yeovil, Somerset, BA22 7LN
Tel 01963 440315   Fax 01963 440901
These are suppliers for the adventurous. They will send, by courier, exotic meats which include wild boar, kangaroo, emu, bison, peacock, crocodile, guinea fowl, wild rabbit, alligator etc.......

Shepherds Purse Speciality Cheeses Ltd.
Leachfield Grange, Newsham, Thirsk, North Yorks, YO7 4DJ
Tel 01845 587220   Contact Nigel or Judy Bell
This family business supplies a wonderful variety of sheep and goat cheeses

---

Life Style Health Care Ltd
Centenary Business Park, Henley-on-Thames,
Oxfordshire, RG9 1DS
Tel 01491 570000   Fax 01491 570001
A good selection of alternative foods for special health diets and people with multiple allergies. Phone or write for a catalogue showing what is available by mail order.

The Soil Association
Bristol House, 40 - 56 Victoria Street, Bristol, BS1 6BY
A very helpful book is available, listing the addresses of farmers and growers of fresh, organic produce who will sell direct to the public. They are listed by county making it easy to find people in your area. At time of going to press the book cost £7.95 (£9.00 inc. p.p.)
Tel 0117 9290661   Contact. Mail Order Dept

If you choose to begin growing your own organic produce you will obtain good advice from:-
HDRA   (Henry Doubleday)
Ryton Organic Gardens, Coventry, CV8 3LG
Tel 024 76303517 or www. hdra. org. uk for catalogue

Candida Control Packs of Vitamins, Minerals, Probiotics and Anti fungal Supplements are obtainable from :-
Earthdust Products
13, Glenwood Gardens,
Hope Corner Lane,
Taunton,
Somerset, TA2 7PA
Tel/Fax 01823 351108   Contact: Debbie Wright

Just Wholefoods
Unit 16, Cirencester Business Est., Elliott Rd, Love Lane, Cirencester, Gloucestershire GL7 1YG
Suppliers of a variety of mixes and whole food items including yeast free stock powder, and colorant and sugar free custard powder. Not all of their mixes are suitable for Candida sufferers. Choose from Cous Cous, Biriyani or Falafel. Also available from some health shops. List available.
Tel 01285 651910   Fax 01285 650266   Contact Anne Madden.

Penny Davenport
"Woodlands", London Road, Battle, East Sussex, TN33 0LP
Supplier of useful items of kitchen equipment to help cope with a specialist diet. Also a yeast free raising agent for making yeast free bread.
Tel 01423 774103   For current catalogue

Paul's Speciality Breads
66 - 68 Snow Hill Ind. Est., Melton Mowbray, Leicester. LE13 1PD
The pumpernickel bread and sour dough breads made by this company are ideal for the Candida diet. Also a variety of wheat free breads available.
Tel 01664 560572   Fax 01664 410345   Ask for list.

Wholistic Research Company
The Old Forge, Mill Green, Hatfield, Herts., AL9 5NZ
Stockists of water filter systems and purifiers, juice extractors and other kitchen appliances, air ionisers, colon health systems, pulsars for energy, and wide range of books and much more that will prove useful to people battling their way back to good health.
Tel 01707 262686   Web www.wholisticresearch. com.
Contact: Fleur Leach   or   Caroline Evans

INDEX OF RECIPES

Page No.

Biscuits

Aunties Oaties 140

Ginger Biscuits 141

Yearnshire Cookies 140

Breads

Garlic Bread 135

Mexican Tortillas 136

Mixed Flour Bread 137

Pitta Bread 132

Pizza Base 136

Seeded Sandwich Bread 135

Soda Bread 132

Sorgham Bread 137

Breakfasts

Asparagus Omelette 34

Baked Beans (home-made) 84

Breakfast in a glass 83

Brown Rice Porridge 35

Bubble and Squeak 85

Farmhouse Scramble 36

Granola 85

Hearty Start 83

Herb Fish Cakes 39

Onion Hash Browners 34

Polenta Maizemeal Porridge 35

Swiss Rosti Potatoes 36

Swiss Style Muesli 35

Cakes

Coconut Rice Fingers 138

Spicy Come Again Cake 139

Page No

Sponge Cakes 139

Welsh Cakes 138

Desserts

Apple and Pear Crumble 120

Beet Treat 72

Carrot Crunch 72

Chocolate Sponge and Sauce 123

Citrus Sorbet 122

Custard 71

Fresh Fruit Salad 119

Granny's Home Made
  Blueberry Pie 124

Minted Apple Snow 121

Plain Yogurt 72

Soya Ice Cream 118

Spicy Surprise 120

Yogurt Ice Cream 118

Yogurt Snow 121

Dips

Guacomole 130

Hummus 42

Tzatsiki 74

Dressings

French Dressing 145

Garlic Dressing 145

Greek Island Dressing 144

Green Yogurt Dressing 145

Mayonnaise 146

Mustard Dressing 144

Yogurt Salad Dressing 144

	Page No.		Page No
Drinks		Plate Pizza	105
Bloody Mary	147	Poussins with Herb Sauce	60
Chamomile Tea	78	Roast Fowl	55
Fruit Juices	147	Roast Meat	54
Fruit Teas	147	Savoury Mince	
Hot Vegetable Broth	78	(Shepherds Pie)	61
Hot Cocoa	78	Scandinavian Mackerel	62
Mint Tea	77	Stir Fry Vegetables	59
Parsley Tea	77	Stuffed Marrow	54
Pink Gin	147	Trout with Almonds	63
Spring Water	147	**Nuts**	146
Dumplings	143	**Pastry**	
Garlic 'Butter'	135	Dessert Pastry	142
Gravy	131	Savoury Pastry	142
Main Meals		**Salads**	
Beef with Orange	102	Beef & Green Rice Salad	101
Chicken Stir Fry	59	Cauliflower & Apple Crunch	99
Columbian Turkey	64	Cold Rice Salad	
Fish Boulangére	105	(Packed Lunches)	162
Fried Chicken in Ginger		Coleslaw	53
& Paprika	60	Exotic Duck Salad	96
Guinea Fowl with		Hot Chinese Chicken Salad	52
Raspberries	102	King Prawn or Scampi	
Haddock with Cheese		and Jícama Salad	51
and Leek Sauce	56	Mixed Bean Salad	52
Lambs Liver with Onions	55	Salmon and Pasta	101
Lamb Provencal	106	Spanakoriso Salad	53
Lasagne	103	Special Potato Salad	95
Mediterranean Fish Stew	110	Tabbouleh	99
Moussaka	104	Zesty Courgette and	
Pan Fried Pizza	109	Chick Pea Salad	100

Sauces	Page No.		Page No
Basic Cheese Sauce	71	Watercress Soup	49
Basic White Sauce	71	**Starters/Lunches**	
Chocolate Sauce	123	Avocado with Dressed	
Snacks		Prawns	40
Corn and Potato Sticks	125	Baba Ghanoush	46
Crudités	74	Cretan Feta Cheese Salad	45
Garlic and Onion Crisps	126	Egg Mayonnaise	40
Garlic Flavoured Popcorn	125	Falafel	41
Jamaican Cornmeal Pone	127	Fish Roe Stuffed Eggs	45
Oat Flapjacks	127	Greek Hummus	42
Oat Muffins	128	Mexican Stuffed Tomatoes	86
Savoury Corn Nibbles	128	Oeufs Florentine	42
Shepherds Omelette	73	Prawn (Shrimp) Apple	
Sprouted Seeds	73	and Celery Cocktail	86
Waffles	129	Ratatouille	87
Soups and Stews		White Bait	46
Avgolemono Soup	95	**Vegetarian Main Meals**	
Celery Soup	48	Aduki Bean Crumble	66
Chicken and Leek Soup	47	Caponata Style Fetuccini	112
Chicken Stew	50	Cauliflower Cheese	68
Chilled Avocado Soup	91	Chilli Bean Casserole	114
Chilled Cucumber Soup	48	Couscous and Curried	
Creamy Carrot Soup	47	Vegetables	70
French Onion Soup	94	Jacket Potatoes	116
Greek Vegetable Soup	49	Parsnip Chips	66
Italian Minestrone Soup	93	Spanish Omelette	111
Leek and Potato Soup	91	Spiced Chick Peas	115
New England Fish Chowder	92	Spinach and Soft Sheeps	
Pot-au-feu		Cheese Quiche	67
(French Beef Stew)	88	Spinach Timbale	69
Warming Winter Stew		Stuffed Kohlrabi	117
(Packed Lunches)	161	Vegetable Curry	113

By the Same Author

The A-Z of coping with M.E. Candida and allergies

"THE WAY BACK"

By Jo Hampton

Simple to follow self help advice

Written by a practitioner and ex-sufferer who really understands her subject. It is everything you need to know in one volume. Written in down to earth language it contains easy to follow advice on vitamin, mineral and probiotic supplementation, a carefully balanced 7 day diet plan and sensible suggestions on how to deal with everyday problems that sufferers face.

Invaluable!   A must!

Ask for it in your health shop or local book store.

ISBN 0 9521544 0 4   **£8.95**

WHAT THE READERS SAY . . . .

". . . fascinating book . . . full of practical advice."
MAURICE NEWBOUND (President of the Natural Health Network)

". . . book is great, best on M.E.Candida and allergy I have read . . . . . . love to sell it in my practice."
JILL JOEL (Practitioner, Queensland, Australia)

". . . a great help . . . constantly refer to it . . ."
MRS. M.G. VIGORS (Sufferer, Lincolnshire)

". . . gave me encouragement and help to go on fighting back . . ."
E. EYKELBOSCH (Sufferer, Essex)

". . .the supplements suggested REALLY WORKED."
R.F. (Sufferer, Sussex)

Kingston House Publishing
13 Glenwood Gardens, Hope Corner Lane, Taunton
Somerset TA2 7PA Telephone/ Fax 01823 35 11 08